GEOMETRY
Second Edition

Assignments

Carnegie Learning

Carnegie Learning >

437 Grant St., Suite 2000
Pittsburgh, PA 15219
Phone 412.690.2442
Customer Service Phone 877.401.2527
Fax 412.690.2444

www.carnegielearning.com

Acknowledgments

We would like to thank those listed here who helped prepare the **Geometry** Assignments.

Jaclyn Snyder, Author
William Hadley, Author
The Carnegie Learning Curriculum Development Team:
- Sandy Bartle, Senior Academic Officer
- David Dengler, Director, Curriculum Development
- David Rivera, Math Editor
- Lezlee Ross, Curriculum Developer

The Carnegie Learning Software Development Team
Mathematical Expressions
The BookMasters® Group

Cover Art: Architects used geometry in several ways to create the interior shown on the front cover. The parallel, symmetrical design of the ceiling beams is both structurally strong and pleasing to the eye. The wall and stairs incorporate right angles and symmetrically inlaid designs. The arches can be described as chords of circles. The staircase suggests our pedagogical approach to geometry: By following the footsteps of Euclid, students can ascend in their understanding of the mathematics. As you work through Carnegie Learning **Geometry**, you will see additional opportunities for using math in your everyday activities.

Cover photo © istockphoto/sagaYago

ISBN: 978-1-60972-143-5
Assignments

Printed in the United States of America
5-5/2013 B&B

Assignment

Name _____ Date _____

Let's Get This Started
Points, Lines, Planes, Rays, and Segments

1. Identify each of the following in the figure shown.

   a. Name all points.

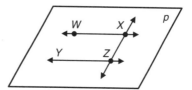

   b. Name all lines.

   c. Name all planes.

2. Identify each of the following in the figure shown.

   a. Name all collinear points.

   b. Name all coplanar lines.

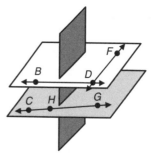

   c. Name all skew lines.

3. Identify each of the following in the figure shown.

   a. Name all rays and identify each endpoint.

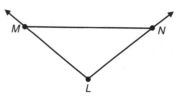

   b. Name all line segments and identify the endpoints.

4. Explain the differences among sketching a geometric figure, drawing a geometric figure, and constructing a geometric figure.

5. Sketch two planes whose intersection is a line.

6. Sketch three planes whose intersection is a point.

7. Draw and label three collinear points *X*, *Y*, and *Z* such that point *Y* is between points *X* and *Z* and the distance between points *X* and *Y* is one half the distance between points *Y* and *Z*.

Name _____   Date _____

Use a symbol to represent the name of each geometric figure in Questions 8 through 10.

8.

9.

10.

11. Draw and label segment *AB* such that it is 3.5 inches long. Then construct and label segment *CD* such that it is congruent to segment *AB*. Write a congruence statement to show the relationship between the two segments.

Assignment

Name _____   Date _____

All About Angles
Naming Angles, Classifying Angles, Duplicating Angles, and Bisecting Angles

1. Write two alternate names for each angle.

a. ∠1

b. ∠3

c. ∠LBH

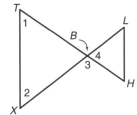

2. Determine the measure of each angle. Then classify the angle as acute, obtuse, right, or straight.

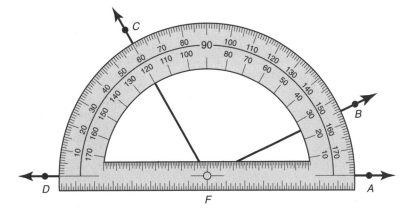

a. $m\angle AFB =$

b. $m\angle BFC =$

c. $m\angle DFB =$

d. $m\angle DFA =$

3. Use a protractor to draw an angle with a measure of 90 degrees. What type of angle is this?

4. Use a protractor to determine the measure of each pair of angles. Then tell whether the angles are congruent. If the angles are congruent, write a congruence statement.

a.

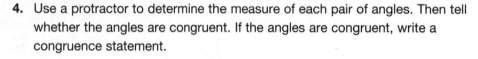

b.

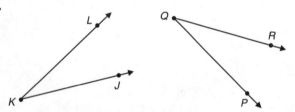

5. Construct an angle with a measure that is three times the measure of $\angle N$.

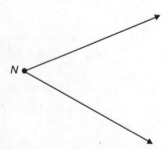

6. Construct an angle with a measure that is one fourth the measure of ∠*W*.

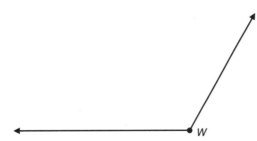

1

Assignment

Name _____ Date _____

Special Angles
Complements, Supplements, Midpoints, Perpendiculars, and Perpendicular Bisectors

1. Use a protractor to draw a pair of supplementary angles that do not share a common side. Label each angle with its measure.

2. Use a protractor to draw a pair of complementary angles that share a common side. Label each angle with its measure.

3. Suppose that $m\angle A = 66°$, $\angle B$ is complementary to $\angle A$, and $\angle C$ is supplementary to $\angle B$. What are the measures of angles B and C?

4. The variables *x* and *y* in the figure represent the measures of angles. Solve for *x* and *y*.

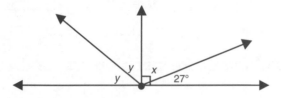

5. The variables *a* and *b* in the figure represent the measures of angles. Solve for *a* and *b*.

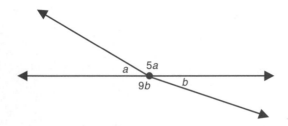

6. Use segment *PQ* to answer the following questions.

P   Q

a. Construct a perpendicular bisector to $\overline{PQ}$ and label the bisector $\overleftrightarrow{RS}$.

b. Label the midpoint *M*.

   c. What is the measure of angle *RMP*?

   d. Suppose that the length of $\overline{PM}$ is 6 units. What is the length of $\overline{QM}$?

7. Construct and label segment *AB*. Then construct perpendicular bisectors so that segment *AB* is divided into four congruent segments.

1

8. Name all pairs of adjacent angles in the figure.

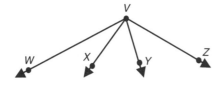

9. What is the difference between two supplementary angles and two angles that form a linear pair?

10. What is the difference between two adjacent angles and two angles that form a linear pair?

11. Identify each of the following in the figure.

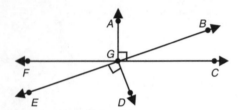

a. Name two pairs of complementary angles.

b. Name six pairs of supplementary angles.

c. Name four pairs of angles that form linear pairs.

d. Name two pairs of vertical angles.

Assignment

Name _____ Date _____

A Little Dash of Logic
Two Methods of Logical Reasoning

Joseph reads a journal article that states that yogurt with live cultures greatly helps digestion and prevents problems associated with lactose intolerance. He notices that his mother has problems with digestion and is lactose intolerant. He suggests that she try eating yogurt because he thinks it may help her feel better.

1. What is the specific information in this situation?

2. What is the general information in this situation?

3. What is the conclusion in this situation?

4. Did Joseph use inductive or deductive reasoning to make his conclusion? Explain.

5. Is Joseph's conclusion correct? Explain.

Sadie reads an article that gives statistics about American families. She learns that the average American family has 2 parents and 2.3 children. She concludes that her neighbors, who are average Americans, probably have 2.3 children.

6. What is the specific information in this situation?

7. What is the general information in this situation?

8. What is the conclusion in this situation?

9. Did Sadie use inductive or deductive reasoning to make her conclusion? Explain.

10. Is Sadie's conclusion correct? Explain.

Nick watches baseball games on television. He noticed that the last five times that the Wolverines played against the Spartans, the Spartans won. Nick concludes that the Spartans always win against the Wolverines.

11. What is the specific information in this situation?

© 2010 Carnegie Learning, Inc.

12. What is the general information in this situation?

13. What is the conclusion in this situation?

14. Did Nick use inductive or deductive reasoning to reach his conclusion? Explain.

15. Is Nick's conclusion correct? Explain.

Lena has noticed that sometimes her face swells after she eats. She thinks she may be allergic to a type of food, so she takes careful notes over the next month, writing down all the ingredients of each meal and noting when her face swells. Reviewing her notes, she finds that the only common ingredient in the meals she ate previous to her face swelling was coconut. Lena concludes that she is allergic to coconut.

16. What is the specific information in this situation?

17. What is the general information in this situation?

18. What is the conclusion in this situation?

19. Did Lena use inductive or deductive reasoning to reach her conclusion? Explain.

20. Is Lena's conclusion correct? Explain.

1

Chaun is looking through records at a record store with her friend Ronaldo. She comes across a record she has not heard by a band she enjoys. Ronaldo knows that Chaun has five records at home by this band and that she likes all of them. He concludes that she will probably like any record made by this band. He tells Chaun so. She buys the record, saying to herself, "I will probably like this record, because I like records made by this band."

21. What conclusion did Ronaldo make? Why?

22. What type of reasoning did Ronaldo use? Explain.

23. What conclusion did Chaun make? Why?

24. What type of reasoning did Chaun use? Explain.

25. Is Ronaldo's conclusion definitely true? Is Chaun's conclusion definitely true? Explain.

The first five numbers in a sequence are 7, 21, 63, 189, and 567.

26. What is the next number in the sequence? How did you calculate the next number?

27. What type or types of reasoning did you use to find the next number? Explain the reasoning you used and the order of your conclusions.

1

Assignment

Name _____   Date _____

Conditionals
Conditional Statements, Postulates, and Theorems

1. Use the following statement to answer each question.

   The sum of the measures of angle *A* and angle *B* is 90 degrees. Therefore, the angles are complementary.

   a. Write the conditional statement in propositional form.

   b. Identify the hypothesis and the conclusion of the conditional statement.

   c. If the hypothesis and conclusion of the conditional statement are both false, what does this mean in terms of the conditional statement?

   d. What is the truth value of the conditional statement if the hypothesis and conclusion are both false?

2. Sketch a figure to illustrate the given conditional statement. Then rewrite the conditional statement by separating the hypothesis and conclusion into "Given" information and "Prove" information.

   If $\angle AXB$ is a right angle and $\overrightarrow{XY}$ bisects $\angle AXB$, then $m\angle AXY = 45°$ and $m\angle BXY = 45°$.

   Given:

   Prove:

3. Describe the differences among Euclidean geometry, hyperbolic geometry, and elliptic geometry when studying two straight lines.

4. Sketch and label a figure to illustrate the Linear Pair Postulate. Then use the Linear Pair Postulate to write a symbolic statement about the figure.

5. Use the Segment Addition Postulate to write four different statements about the figure shown.

6. Name the postulate that tells you that $m\angle FGH + m\angle HGJ = m\angle FGJ$ in the figure shown.

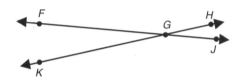

7. Name the postulate that tells you that $m\angle XYW + m\angle ZYW = 180°$ in the figure shown.

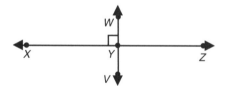

8. Name the postulate that tells you that $m\overline{RL} + m\overline{LT} = m\overline{RT}$ in the figure shown.

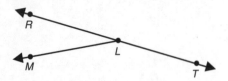

Assignment

Name _____ Date _____

Forms of Proof
Paragraph Proof, Two-Column Proof, Construction Proof, and Flow Chart Proof

Identify the property that justifies each statement.

1. If $\overline{AB} \cong \overline{PR}$ and $\overline{PR} \cong \overline{ST}$, then $\overline{AB} \cong \overline{ST}$.

2. If $JK = 6$ centimeters and $CD = 6$ centimeters, then $JK = CD$.

3. Angle ABC is congruent to angle ABC.

4. If $m\angle3 = m\angle1$, then $m\angle3 + m\angle2 = m\angle1 + m\angle2$.

5. Enter the reasons to complete the two-column proof below.

    Given: $\angle1 \cong \angle4$

    Prove: $\angle2 \cong \angle3$

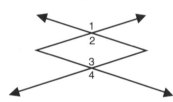

Statements	Reasons
1. $\angle1 \cong \angle4$	1.
2. $\angle4 \cong \angle3$	2.
3. $\angle1 \cong \angle2$	3.
4. $\angle1 \cong \angle3$	4.
5. $\angle2 \cong \angle3$	5.

6. The boxes below show the parts of a flow chart proof. Rearrange the boxes and draw arrows to connect the boxes in a logical sequence to prove the statement below.

Given: $FG = JK$

Given: $GH = HJ$

Prove: $FH = HK$

F ●————————————● ● ● ————————————● K
                     G H J

$FG + GH = GH + JK$ Addition Property of Equality

$FH = HK$ Substitution

$FG = JK$ Given

$GH = HJ$ Given

$HJ + JK = HK$ Segment Addition Postulate

$GH = GH$ Identity Property

$FG + GH = HJ + JK$ Substitution

$FG + GH = FH$ Segment Addition Postulate

7. Write a paragraph proof to prove the statement below.

Given: $m\angle QRS = 90°$

Given: $\angle RTS \cong \angle QRT$

Prove: $\angle RTS$ and $\angle TRS$ are complementary.

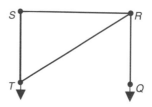

8. Use a construction to prove the statement below.

Given: Line ST is a perpendicular bisector of $\overline{XZ}$.

Given: $XV = WZ$

Prove: $VY = YW$

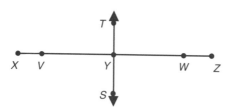

9. In the figure, $\angle GXF \cong \angle CXD$.

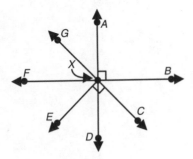

a. What theorem tells you that $\angle AXG \cong \angle CXD$?

b. What theorem tells you that $\angle EXF \cong \angle EXD$?

c. What theorem tells you that $\angle GXD \cong \angle CXF$?

Assignment

Name _____ Date _____

Transversals and Lines
Angles Formed by Transversals of Parallel and
Non-Parallel Lines

1. Sketch a figure that shows three lines in the same plane whose intersection is a single point.

2. Use the figure to identify each of the following.

   a. Two pairs of parallel segments

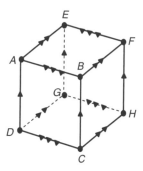

   b. Two pairs of skew segments

b. Identify all pairs of alternate interior angles.

c. Identify all pairs of alternate exterior angles.

d. Identify all pairs of same side interior angles.

e. Identify all pairs of same side exterior angles.

f. Identify all pairs of corresponding angles.

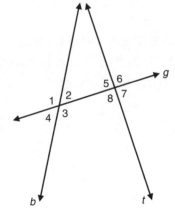

4. Use the figure to classify each pair of angles.

a. ∠1 and ∠14

b. ∠6 and ∠8

c. ∠12 and ∠15

d. ∠10 and ∠11

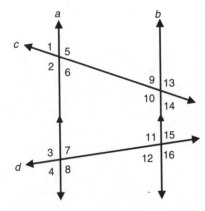

© 2010 Carnegie Learning, Inc.

5. Give an example of a real-life situation that involves skew lines or line segments. Draw a sketch to support your answer.

6. Give an example of a real-life situation that involves parallel lines or line segments. Draw a sketch to support your answer.

2

Assignment

Name _____ Date _____

Making Conjectures
Conjectures about Angles Formed by Parallel Lines
Cut by a Transversal

1. Construct line *p* parallel to line *b* such that line *m* is a transversal.

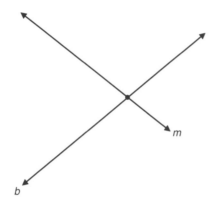

Use the given information to determine the measures of angles 2 through 8.

2. $p \parallel q$ and $m\angle 1 = 54°$

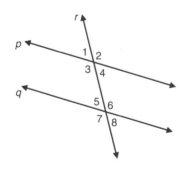

3. $s \parallel t$ and $m\angle 1 = 137°$

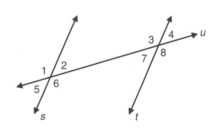

4. Write an expression for the measure of each numbered angle in the figure.

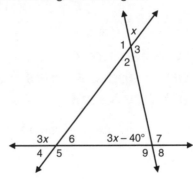

Solve for *x* in each figure.

5.

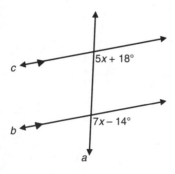

6.

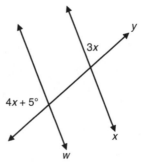

Name _____ Date _____

7. Suppose that two parallel lines are intersected by a transversal and all corresponding angles are supplementary. How is this possible? Sketch and label a figure to support your answer.

2

Assignment

Name _____ Date _____

What's Your Proof?
Alternate Interior Angle Theorem, Alternate Exterior Angle Theorem, Same-Side Interior Angle Theorem, and Same-Side Exterior Angle Theorem

Determine the relationship between the indicated angles and write a postulate or theorem that justifies your answer.

1. Angles 2 and 8

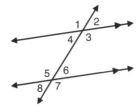

2. Angles 6 and 7

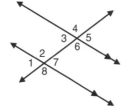

3. Angles 1 and 4

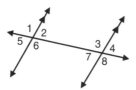

4. Angles 4 and 5

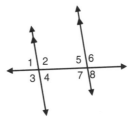

5. In the figure at the right, what postulate or theorem tells you that $x + y = 180°$?

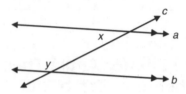

6. Suppose that the measure of angle 1 is 43 degrees. Determine the measures of angles 2 through 8.

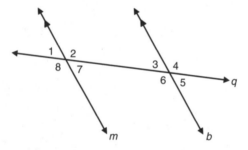

7. The following boxes show the parts of a flow chart proof of the Same-Side Interior Angle Theorem. Rearrange the boxes and draw arrows to connect the boxes in a logical sequence to prove the Same-Side Interior Angle Theorem.

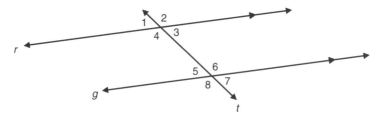

> Angles 1 and 4 are a linear pair.
> Linear Pair Postulate

> $m\angle 1 = m\angle 5$
> Definition of congruent angles

> $r \parallel g$
> Given

> $\angle 5$ and $\angle 4$ are supplementary
> Definition of supplementary angles

> $m\angle 5 + m\angle 4 = 180°$
> Substitution

> $m\angle 1 + m\angle 4 = 180°$
> Definition of linear pair

> $\angle 1 \cong \angle 5$
> Corresponding Angles Postulate

8. Use the figure to determine the measure of each indicated angle.

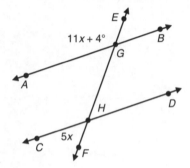

a. $m\angle EGA$

b. $m\angle CHF$

c. $m\angle FHD$

d. $m\angle EGB$

9. Suppose that two parallel lines are intersected by a transversal and all same side interior angles are congruent. How is this possible? Sketch and label a figure to support your answer.

Assignment

Name _____   Date _____

A Reversed Condition
Parallel Line Converse Theorems

1. Use the figure to write the postulate or theorem that justifies each statement.

   a. $m\angle 1 = m\angle 8$, so $a \parallel b$

   b. $m\angle 4 + m\angle 6 = 180°$, so $a \parallel b$

   c. $a \parallel b$, so $m\angle 3 = m\angle 7$

   d. $m\angle 2 + m\angle 8 = 180°$, so $a \parallel b$

   e. $m\angle 4 = m\angle 5$, so $a \parallel b$

   f. $a \parallel b$, so $m\angle 3 + m\angle 5 = 180°$

2. Use the given information to determine the pair of lines that are parallel. Write the postulate or theorem that justifies your answer.

a. $m\angle 4 = m\angle 5$

b. $m\angle 2 + m\angle 12 = 180°$

c. $m\angle 7 = m\angle 11$

d. $m\angle 8 + m\angle 10 = 180°$

e. $m\angle 1 + m\angle 7 = 180°$

f. $m\angle 2 = m\angle 11$

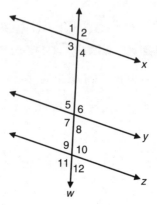

3. Given triangle *ABC* as shown, prove that segment *AB* is parallel to segment *DE*.

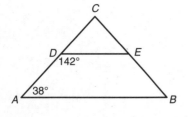

© 2010 Carnegie Learning, Inc.

4. In the figure, $m\angle 1 = (7x - 12)°$, $m\angle 3 = (6x + 4)°$, and $m\angle 8 = (5x)°$. Show that line p is parallel to line q. Explain your reasoning.

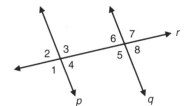

2

Assignment

Name _____ Date _____

Many Sides
Naming Geometric Figures

Classify and name each polygon.

1.

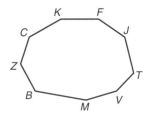

2.

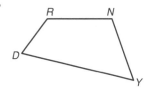

3.

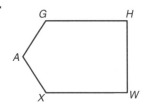

4.

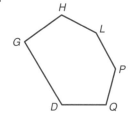

5. Draw an example of a regular pentagon named *ABCDE* that is convex.

6. Draw an example of an irregular octagon named *STUVWXYZ* that is concave.

7. Use the quadrilateral to answer each question.

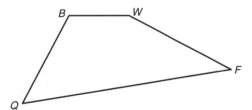

    a. Name two pairs of opposite sides.

    b. Name two pairs of opposite angles.

    c. Name two pairs of consecutive sides.

    d. Name two pairs of consecutive angles.

Draw and name all diagonals of the figure.

8.

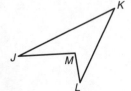

9.

© 2010 Carnegie Learning, Inc.

Determine whether the figure has any reflex angles. If so, name them.

10.

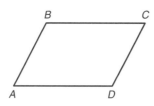

11.

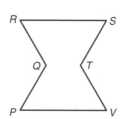

2

Assignment

Name _____ Date _____

Quads and Tris
Classifying Triangles and Quadrilaterals

Draw an example of each polygon described.

1. Right scalene triangle

2. Obtuse isosceles triangle

3. Rhombus

4. Kite

List all types of quadrilaterals that have the given characteristics.

5. All angles are congruent.

6. Opposite sides are congruent.

7. Two pairs of consecutive sides are congruent.

Determine whether each statement is true or false. Explain your answer and draw an example or counterexample, if possible.

8. An obtuse triangle can be a scalene triangle.

9. All parallelograms are rectangles.

10. A right triangle can be isosceles.

11. Is it possible to draw an equilateral, obtuse triangle? If so, draw the triangle. If not, explain why not.

12. What type of quadrilateral is both a rhombus and a rectangle? Explain your reasoning.

© 2010 Carnegie Learning, Inc.

● Assignment

Name _____   Date _____

Weaving a Rug
Area and Perimeter of Rectangles and Squares

1. An artist is weaving a rectangular rug to match the pattern shown in the figure.
   Use the figure to answer parts (a) through (e).

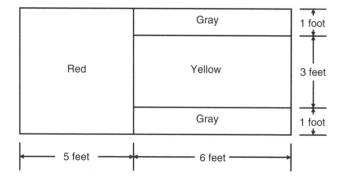

   a. Calculate the area of the yellow region.

   b. Calculate the area of the red region.

   c. Calculate the total area of the gray regions.

   d. Calculate the area of the entire rug. Show your calculation in two different ways.

   e. Suppose that the artist wants to add a braid trim around the edges of the rug.
      How many feet of braid trim will the artist need?

2. Suppose you want to paint a rectangular mural. You want the perimeter of the mural to be 32 feet. Sketch three rectangles on the grid shown to represent three possible sizes for your mural. Each square on the grid represents a square that is one foot long and one foot wide. Which of the three murals has the greatest area? Which of the three murals has the least area? Show your work.

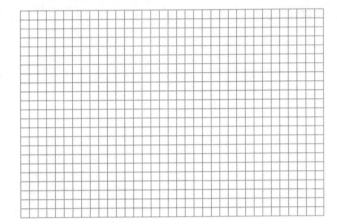

3. A rectangle has an area of 126 square centimeters and a width of 9 centimeters. What is the length of the rectangle?

4. A square has a perimeter of 68 inches. What is the length of a side of the square?

5. A rectangle has an area of 36 square feet and a length that is 4 times the width. What are the dimensions of the rectangle?

3

Assignment

Name _____ Date _____

Boundary Lines
Area of Parallelograms and Triangles

Calculate the area of each figure. Each square on the grid represents a
square that is one meter long and one meter wide.

1.

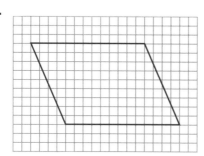

2.

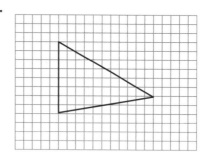

3. An artist receives a request from a client to create a rug that is the shape of a
   parallelogram. The artist charges $25 per square foot of rug. The client decides to
   pay $600 for the rug. Draw two different designs for the rug on the grid. What is the
   area, base, and height of each rug? Show your work.

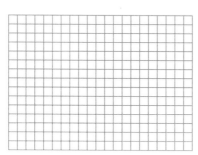

4. You are making a kite out of nylon fabric. The height of the kite will be 36 inches and the widest part of the kite will be 24 inches as shown in the diagram. How much nylon fabric will you need to make the kite? Write the answer in square inches and square feet.

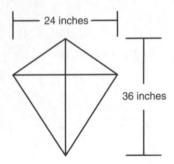

5. The sail on a boat is triangular and its area is 216 square feet. The base of the sail is 18 feet. What is the height of the sail?

6. A triangular window in a beach house has a height of 48 inches and contains 1728 square inches of glass. What is the base of the window?

3

Assignment

Name _____   Date _____

The Keystone Effect
Area of a Trapezoid

Calculate the area of each trapezoid. Each square on the grid represents a square that is one inch long and one inch wide.

1.

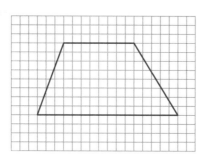

2.

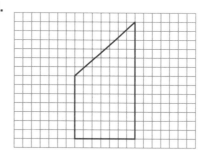

3. The height of a trapezoid is 7 inches and the bases are 7 inches and 17 inches. What is the area of the trapezoid?

4. Can the bases of a trapezoid be the same length? Explain.

5. The area of a trapezoid is 209 square yards and the bases are 15 yards and 23 yards. What is the height of the trapezoid?

6. The area of a trapezoid is 150 square meters. The height is 10 meters and one base is two meters longer than the other base. What is each base?

7. The area of a trapezoid is 252 square feet. The height is 24 feet and one base is twice the length of the other base. What is each base?

8. The height of a trapezoid is 4 units and the bases are 3 units and 7 units.

   a. Draw the trapezoid on the grid below if the trapezoid is isosceles. Then calculate the area of the trapezoid.

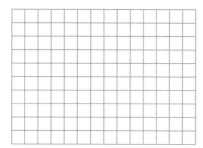

   b. Draw the trapezoid on the grid below if the trapezoid contains one right angle. Then calculate the area of the trapezoid.

3

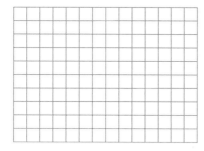

   c. Do the trapezoids in parts (a) and (b) have the same area? Explain.

Assignment

Name _____ Date _____

Signs, Signs, Every Place There Are Signs!
Area of Regular Polygons

Calculate the area of each regular polygon.

1.

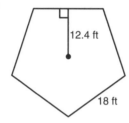

12.4 ft

18 ft

2.

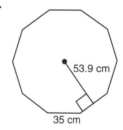

53.9 cm

35 cm

3. A regular heptagon has a side length of 24 inches and an apothem of 24.9 inches. What is the area of the regular heptagon?

4. A stop sign has a perimeter of 160 inches and an apothem of 24.1 inches. What is the area of the stop sign?

5. A regular nonagon has an area of 378 square yards and an apothem of 10.5 yards. What is the length of a side of the regular nonagon?

6. A regular polygon has an area of 10,080 square meters. The length of a side of the polygon is 30 meters and the apothem is 56 meters. What type of regular polygon is this?

7. A quilt is made by sewing together pieces of material that are shaped like regular hexagons. Each hexagon has an apothem of 1.7 inches and a perimeter of 12 inches. About how many regular hexagons will it take to make a quilt that is a 6-foot by 8-foot rectangle? Show all your work.

Assignment

Name _____ Date _____

Say Cheese!
Area and Circumference of a Circle

Calculate the circumference and area of each circle. Use 3.14 to approximate π. Each square on the grid represents a square that is one centimeter long and one centimeter wide.

1.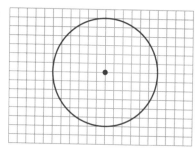

2.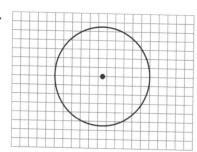

3. A circle has a diameter of 34 inches. What are the circumference and radius of the circle? Write your answers in terms of π.

4. A circle has a radius of 15 feet. What are the circumference and area of the circle? Write your answers in terms of π.

5. Complete the table. Use 3.14 to approximate π.

Circle	Radius	Diameter	Circumference	Area
Circle A	1 ft			
Circle B		56 m		
Circle C				200.96 yd²
Circle D			100.48 in.	

6. What is the area of the annulus shown? Use 3.14 to approximate π.

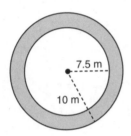

7.5 m

10 m

7. Suppose that x represents the radius of circle A in inches. The radius of circle B is three times the radius of circle A. Use this information to answer the following questions.

a. Write an expression for the diameter of circle A.

b. Write an expression for the radius of circle B.

c. Write an expression for the diameter of circle B.

d. Write expressions in terms of π for the circumferences of circles A and B. How does the circumference of circle B compare to the circumference of circle A?

e. Write expressions for the areas of circles A and B. How does the area of circle B compare to the area of circle A?

3

Assignment

Name _____   Date _____

Installing Carpeting and Tile
Area and Perimeter of Composite Figures

Calculate the area of each figure. Use 3.14 to approximate π.

1.

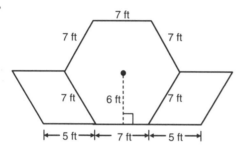

2.

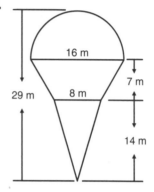

Draw an example of each term.

3. circle

4. polygon

5. composite figure

6. area

Assignment

Name _____ Date _____

Interior and Exterior Angles of a Triangle
Triangle Sum, Exterior Angle, and Exterior Angle
Inequality Theorems

1. Determine the measure of angle *UPM* in the following figure. Explain your reasoning and show all your work.

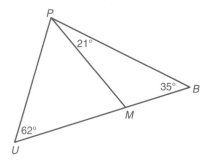

2. In the following figure, $\overrightarrow{AB}$ is parallel to $\overrightarrow{DE}$. Determine the measure of each missing angle in the figure.

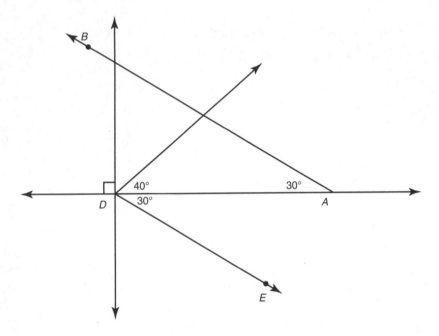

3. You are building a triangular play area for your new puppy. You decide that the play area will have angle measures of 50 degrees and 40 degrees as shown in the following figure.

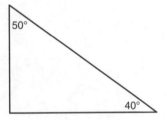

a. Which side of the play area is the longest?

b. Which side of the play area is the shortest?

c. Explain how you determined your answers in parts (a) and (b).

Solve for x.

4.

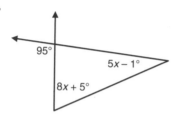

5.

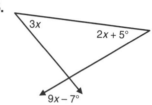

4

6. Use the figure to write a paragraph proof of the Exterior Angle Inequality Theorem.

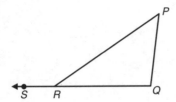

Given: Triangle *PQR* with exterior angle *PRS*

Prove: $m\angle PRS > m\angle P$ and $m\angle PRS > m\angle Q$

Assignment

Name _____ Date _____

Installing a Satellite Dish
Simplifying Radicals, Pythagorean Theorem,
and Its Converse

Determine the side length of each square tile. Use a complete sentence to explain how you determined your answer.

1.

225 cm²

2.

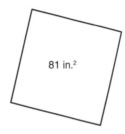

81 in.²

Simplify each radical expression completely.

3. $\sqrt{60}$

4. $\sqrt{28}$

5. $\sqrt{45}$

6. $\sqrt{108}$

7. $\dfrac{1}{\sqrt{5}}$

8. $\dfrac{3}{\sqrt{2}}$

9. $\dfrac{3}{\sqrt{6}}$

10. A helicopter is flying 40 feet above the ocean and spots a man-eating shark directly below. The distance from the shark to the beach is 60 feet. How far is the helicopter from the beach? Show all your work.

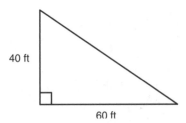

40 ft

60 ft

11. A bird leaves its nest and flies two miles due north, then three miles due east, then four miles due north, and then five miles due east, finally reaching the ocean. How far is its nest from the ocean? Show all your work.

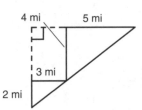

4 mi   5 mi

3 mi

2 mi

12. A tree was planted 15.9 feet from a house and eventually grew to a height of 23 feet. During a particularly bad electrical storm, lightning struck the tree, causing the top of the tree to break off 6 feet above the ground. If the severed part of the tree is falling toward the house, will it hit the house? Use a complete sentence to explain your reasoning.

Name _____ Date _____

13. James Abram Garfield was the 20th President of the United States. He is given credit for proving the Pythagorean Theorem using the area of a trapezoid.

Use the following figure to complete parts (a) through (e).

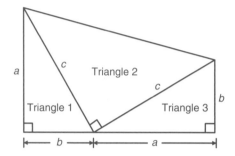

a. Use the formula for the area of a trapezoid to write an expression that represents the area of the trapezoid.

b. Write expressions that represent the areas of Triangles 1, 2, and 3.

c. Write an expression that represents the area of the trapezoid as the sum of the areas of Triangles 1, 2, and 3.

d. Write and simplify an equation that shows the relationship between the expressions you wrote for the area of the trapezoid in parts (a) and (c).

e. Explain how parts (a) through (d) prove the Pythagorean Theorem.

Assignment

Name _____ Date _____

Special Right Triangles
Properties of a 45°–45°–90° Triangle

1. The legs of the isosceles triangle each measure 14 inches.
   Calculate the length of the hypotenuse.

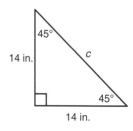

2. Calculate the value of c.

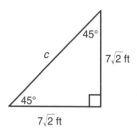

3. The perimeter of the square is 32 centimeters.
   Calculate the length of its diagonal.

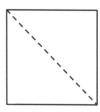

4. Calculate the value of a.

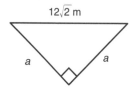

5. The length of a diagonal of the square is 36 centimeters. Calculate the length of each side.

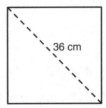

6. The length of a diagonal of the square is 12 centimeters. Calculate the area.

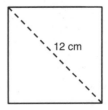

7. Calculate the area of the figure below using the information given in the diagram. The figure is composed of a triangle and a semicircle. Use 3.14 for π.

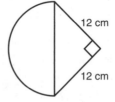

8. The length of a diagonal of the square in the figure below is 60 inches. Calculate the perimeter of the figure. The figure is composed of a square and a semicircle.

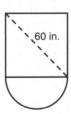

© 2010 Carnegie Learning, Inc.

4

Assignment

Name _____   Date _____

Other Special Right Triangles
Properties of a 30°–60°–90° Triangle

1. The length of the hypotenuse in the 30°–60°–90°
   triangle shown is 28 meters. Calculate the lengths of
   sides *a* and *b*.

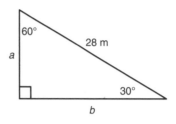

2. The length of the side opposite the 30° angle is 5 feet.
   Calculate the lengths of sides *b* and *c*.

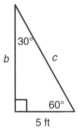

3. The length of the side opposite the 60° angle is
   8 millimeters. Calculate the lengths of sides *a* and *c*.

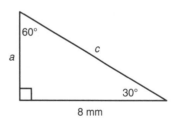

4. A broadcast antenna is situated on top of a tower. The signal travels from the antenna to your house so you can watch TV. The angle of elevation from your house to the tower measures 30° and the distance from your house to the tower is 500 feet. Calculate the height of the tower and the distance the signal travels.

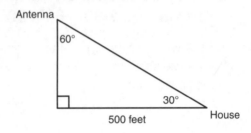

5. The length of the longer leg in the 30°−60°−90° triangle shown is 22 miles. Calculate the length of the hypotenuse.

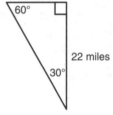

6. The length of the shorter leg in the 30°−60°−90° triangle below is 13 meters. Calculate the length of the hypotenuse.

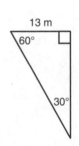

© 2010 Carnegie Learning, Inc.

7. Calculate the perimeter of the trapezoid.

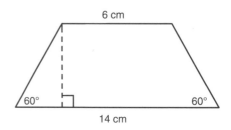

8. Calculate the area of the triangle.

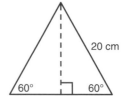

9. Calculate the area of the trapezoid.

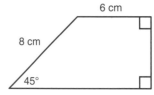

10. A broadcast antenna is situated on top of a tower, and the signal travels from the antenna to your house so that you can watch TV. The angle of elevation from your house to the tower measures 30° and the distance from your house to the tower is 775 feet. Find the height of the tower and the distance the signal travels.

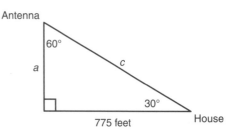

© 2010 Carnegie Learning, Inc.

4

Assignment

Name _____ Date _____

Pasta Anyone?
Triangle Inequality Theorem

1. You are building a triangular pen for baby ducks. The sides of the pen will be made from lumber you have left from other projects. You have two 12-foot boards, one 14-foot board, one 8-foot board, one 4-foot board, one 3-foot board, and one 2-foot board. Use this information to answer parts (a) through (f).

   a. Suppose you choose the 14-foot board and the 4-foot board. Of the boards you have left over, what is the longest board that can be used for the third side of the pen? Explain.

   b. Suppose you choose a 12-foot board and the 8-foot board. Of the boards you have left over, what is the shortest board that can be used for the third side of the pen? Explain.

   c. Suppose you choose a 12-foot board and the 4-foot board. Of the boards you have left over, which board(s) can be used for the third side of the pen? Explain.

d. How many different triangular pens can be formed using the 4-foot board? List the side lengths of each possible triangular pen.

e. If you only have three boards and their lengths are 5 feet, 8 feet, and 4 feet, can you form a triangular pen? Explain.

f. Suppose you decide to build a pen with side lengths of 14 feet, 12 feet, and 8 feet as shown in the figure. Which angle has the greatest measure? Which angle has the least measure? Explain.

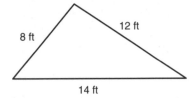

List the angles and sides of each triangle in order from least to greatest. Do not measure the angles or sides.

2.

3.

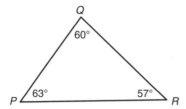

4. Triangle *ABC* with the following: $m\angle A = 27°$, $m\angle B = 119°$, and $m\angle C = 34°$

5. Triangle *RST* with the following: $RS = 8$ cm, $ST = 20$ cm, and $RT = 14$ cm

Determine whether it is possible to form a triangle using segments with the following measurements. Explain.

6. 14 inches, 21 inches, 7 inches

7. 26 feet, 10 feet, 18 feet

8. 2.2 millimeters, 7.2 millimeters, 5.1 millimeters

4

Assignment

Name _____ Date _____

Ace Reporter
Review of Ratio and Proportion

Write a ratio that is equivalent to each ratio.

1. $\dfrac{6}{12} =$

2. $\dfrac{7}{12} =$

3. $\dfrac{4}{15} =$

4. $14:7 =$

5. $3:25 =$

6. $1.25:7 =$

Solve each proportion.

7. $\dfrac{12}{15} = \dfrac{16}{x}$

8. $\dfrac{3.5}{8} = \dfrac{x}{24}$

9. $\dfrac{7}{x} = \dfrac{56}{8}$

10. You are on the refreshment committee for a school dance. The committee decides to serve pizza at the dance and you need to determine the type of pizzas to order. You survey 45 students and get the following results.

    10 students prefer cheese

    26 students prefer pepperoni

    9 students prefer mushroom

    The committee expects about 220 students to attend the dance. Use this information to answer parts (a) through (d).

    a. Set up and solve a proportion to predict the number of students at the dance who will choose cheese pizza.

5

b. Set up and solve a proportion to predict the number of students at the dance who will choose pepperoni pizza.

c. Set up and solve a proportion to predict the number of students at the dance who will choose mushroom pizza.

d. Suppose each pizza is cut into 12 slices and you estimate that each student at the dance will eat 2 slices of pizza. How many of each type of pizza should you order for the dance?

5

Assignment

Name _____ Date _____

Picture Picture on the Wall...
Similar Polygons

Determine whether each pair of polygons is similar. If the polygons are similar, write a similarity statement. Explain your reasoning.

1.

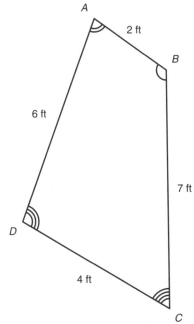

2.

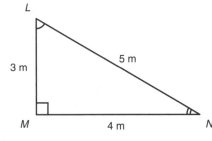

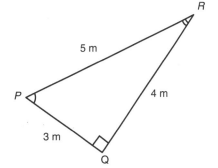

3. While on vacation, you buy a postcard of Niagara Falls. The postcard is a rectangle 6 inches long and 4 inches wide. You want to enlarge the postcard to make a poster to hang on your bedroom wall. You want the length of the poster to be 4 feet. What will be the width of the poster in feet?

4. You are building a model of your neighborhood. The scale of the model is 300:1. In the model, your back yard is a rectangle with a perimeter of 6 inches. What is the actual perimeter of your back yard in feet?

5. Two stops signs are similar. The smaller stop sign has a side length of 12 inches and the larger stop sign has a side length of 16 inches. What is the ratio of the area of the smaller stop sign to the area of the larger stop sign?

Assignment

Name _____ Date _____

To Be or Not To Be Similar?
Similar Triangle Postulates

1. In the figure below, $\overleftrightarrow{NS} \parallel \overleftrightarrow{BE}$. Use the information given in the figure to determine $m\angle SNA$, $m\angle NAS$, $m\angle ABE$ and $m\angle BAE$. Is $\triangle NSA$ similar to $\triangle EBA$? If the triangles are similar, write a similarity statement. Use complete sentences to explain your answers.

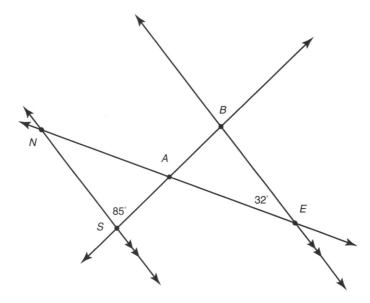

5

2. Use a ruler to determine whether the triangles shown are similar. Explain your answer.

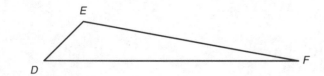

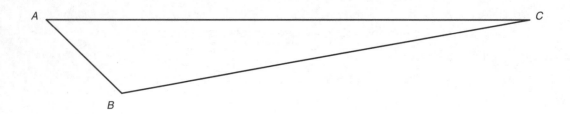

5

3. In the figure shown, $\overline{NU} \parallel \overline{CV}$. Use the figure to complete parts (a) through (c).

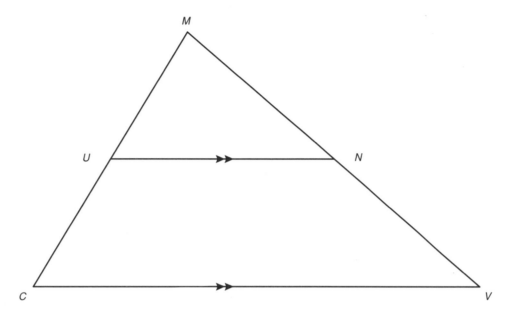

a. Is $\angle MUN \cong \angle MCV$? Explain your answer.

b. Is $\angle MNU \cong \angle MVC$? Explain your answer.

c. Is $\triangle CMV \sim \triangle UMN$? Explain your answer.

4. In the figure shown, segments *AB* and *DE* are parallel. The length of segment *BC* is 10 units and the length of segment *CD* is 5 units. Use this information to calculate the value of *x*. Explain how you found your answer.

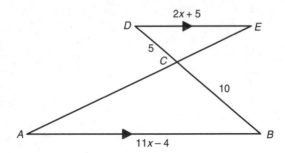

Assignment

Name _____ Date _____

Triangle Side Ratios
Angle Bisector/Proportional Side Theorem

Calculate the indicated length in each figure.

1. $\overline{KN}$ bisects $\angle K$. Calculate *MN*.

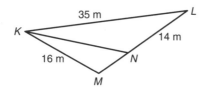

2. $\overline{SQ}$ bisects $\angle S$. Calculate *SR*.

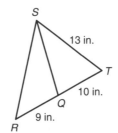

3. Use the figure and the given information to write a paragraph proof of the Angle Bisector/Proportional Side Theorem.

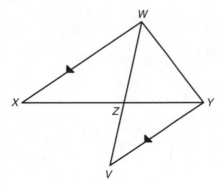

Given: $\overline{WZ}$ bisects $\angle XWY$ and $\overline{XW} \parallel \overline{VY}$

Prove: $\dfrac{WX}{XZ} = \dfrac{WY}{YZ}$

5

4. The figure shows a truss on a bridge. Segment *BF* bisects angle *CBE*. Use this information to determine *EF* and *CF*.

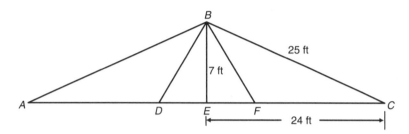

5. The figure shows a truss for a barn roof. Segment *DF* bisects angle *ADB* and segment *EG* bisects angle *CEB*. Triangle *DBE* is an equilateral triangle. Use this information to determine the perimeter of the truss.

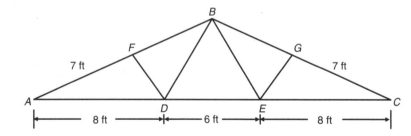

5

Assignment

Name _____ Date _____

Geometric Mean
Similar Right Triangles

Solve for x.

1.

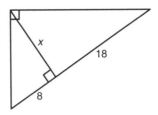

2.

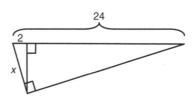

3. Use the figure and the given information to write a paragraph proof of the Right Triangle/Altitude Similarity Theorem.

Given: Triangle *ABC* is a right triangle with altitude *CD*.

Prove: △*ABC* ~ △*ACD* ~ △*CBD*

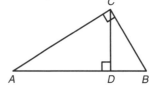

5

4. The geometric mean of two numbers is 20. One of the numbers is 50. What is the other number?

5. The geometric mean of two numbers is $5\sqrt{3}$. One of the numbers is 3. What is the other number?

6. Use the figure and the given information to prove the Right Triangle Altitude Theorem 1.

Given: Triangle ABC is a right triangle with altitude CD.

Prove: $\dfrac{AD}{CD} = \dfrac{CD}{BD}$

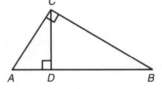

5

7. Use the figure and the given information to prove the Right Triangle Altitude Theorem 2.

Given: Triangle ABC is a right triangle with altitude CD.

Prove: $\dfrac{AB}{AC} = \dfrac{AC}{AD}$ and $\dfrac{AB}{BC} = \dfrac{BC}{BD}$

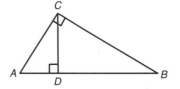

Solve for a, b, and c.

8.

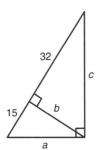

5

9.

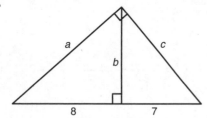

10. You are standing 15 feet from a tree. Your line of sight to the top of the tree and to the bottom of the tree forms a 90-degree angle as shown in the diagram. The distance between your line of sight and the ground is 5 feet. Estimate the height of the tree.

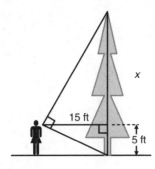

Name _____ Date _____

Indirect Measurement
Application of Similar Triangles

1. You want to measure the height of a tree at the community park. You stand in the tree's shadow so that the tip of your shadow meets the tip of the tree's shadow 2 meters from where you are standing. The distance from the tree to the tip of the tree's shadow is 5.4 meters. You are 1.25 meters tall. Draw a diagram to represent the situation. Then find the height of the tree.

2. You and a friend are making a banner to hang between the apartment buildings, across the street. You each are on the 10th floor of apartment buildings that are directly across the street and have balconies. To hang the banner, you and your friend need to attach it to hooks on the wall of each balcony. The wall of your balcony is 6 feet away from the street and the wall of your friend's balcony is 4 feet away from the street. You also know that your friend's balcony is 10 feet away from the end of his building and your balcony is 100 feet away from the edge of your building. How wide is the street between you and your friend's apartment buildings? How long does the banner need to be? Show all your work and use complete sentences in your answer.

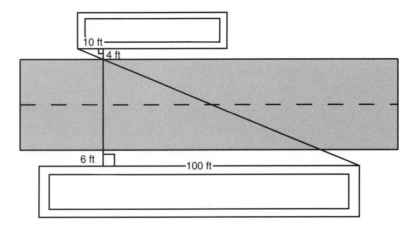

Assignment

Name _____ Date _____

Constructing Congruent Triangles or Not Constructing Triangles

In each exercise, do the following.

  a. **Use the given information to construct a triangle.**

  b. **Determine whether it is possible to use the given information to construct another triangle that is not congruent to the first triangle.**

  c. **If it is possible to construct another triangle that is not congruent to the first triangle, construct it. If it is not possible, explain why not.**

  1. Use the two line segments and the included angle to construct △X′Y′Z′.

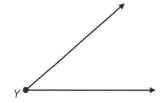

2. Use the three angles to construct △ *J′K′L′*.

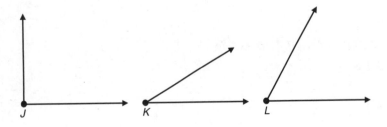

6

3. Use the two angles and the included side to construct $\triangle M'N'P'$.

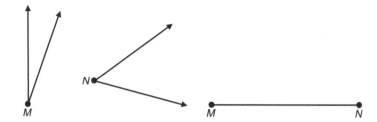

Assignment

Name _____ Date _____

Congruence Theorems
SSS, SAS, ASA, and AAS

1. Complete the proof of the Angle-Side-Angle (ASA) Congruence Theorem.

   Given: $\angle A \cong \angle D$, $\overline{AC} \cong \overline{DF}$, $\angle C \cong \angle F$

   Prove: $\triangle ABC \cong \triangle DEF$

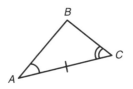 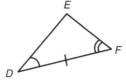

Statements	Reasons
1. $\angle A \cong \angle D$, $\overline{AC} \cong \overline{DF}$, $\angle C \cong \angle F$	1.
2. $\triangle ABC \sim \triangle DEF$	2.
3. $\angle A \cong$ ___ , ___ $\cong \angle E$, $\angle C \cong$	3. Definition of Similar Triangles
4. $\dfrac{AB}{DE} = \dfrac{BC}{EF} = \dfrac{AC}{DF}$	4.
5. $AC = DF$	5.
6. $\dfrac{AC}{DF} =$	6. Division Property of Equality
7. $\dfrac{AB}{} = \dfrac{}{EF} = 1$	7. Substitution
8. $AB = DE$, $BC = EF$	8.
9.	9. Definition of Congruence
10. $\triangle ABC \cong \triangle DEF$	10.

6

2. Write a two-column proof of the Angle-Angle-Side (AAS) Congruence Theorem.

Given: $\angle A \cong \angle D$, $\angle B \cong \angle E$, $\overline{BC} \cong \overline{EF}$,

Prove: $\triangle ABC \cong \triangle DEF$

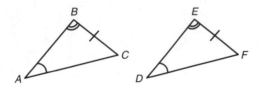

Write a Given statement and state the theorem that proves the triangles are congruent. Then write a congruence statement.

3.

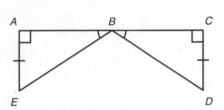

4.

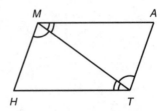

6

Name _____   Date _____

Determine the information that is needed to use the indicated theorem to show that the triangles are congruent.

5. $\triangle FJG = \triangle HJG$ by SAS

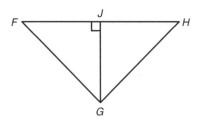

6. $\triangle VWX = \triangle ZYX$ by AAS

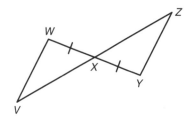

7. The figure shows a basic plan for a decorative porch roof. In the figure, $\overline{DP}$ is perpendicular to $\overline{AG}$ and $\overline{AP} \cong \overline{PG}$. Use a two-column proof to show $\triangle DPA \cong \triangle DPG$.

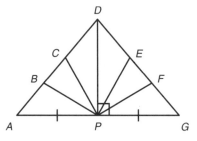

6

6

Assignment

Name _____ Date _____

Right Triangle Congruence Theorems
HL, LL, HA, and LA

Write a Given statement and state the theorem that proves the triangles are congruent. Then write a congruence statement.

1.

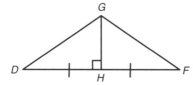

2.

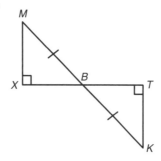

Determine the information that is needed to use the indicated theorem to show that the triangles are congruent.

3. △RQW ≅ △RPW by HL

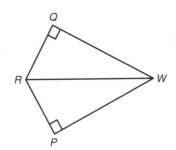

4. △JNZ ≅ △HNC by LA

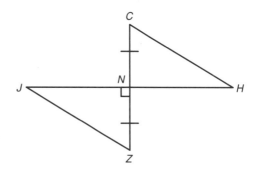

6

5. In the following figure, triangle *ABD* is an isosceles triangle and $\overline{AC}$ is perpendicular to $\overline{BD}$. Use a two-column proof to show that $\angle B \cong \angle D$.

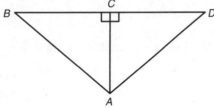

6

Assignment

Name _____ Date _____

CPCTC
Corresponding Parts of Congruent Triangles are Congruent

1. What is the width of the swimming pool? Explain how you got your answer.

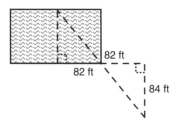

2. Marcel is painting the triangular section of a shuffleboard court shown in the figure. He starts by putting 41 feet of tape around the outside of the triangle. He knows that the base of the triangle is 16 feet and each base angle of the triangle measures 50 degrees. What is the length of each leg?

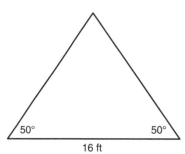

6

Calculate the measure of angle 1. Show your work.

3.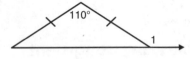

4.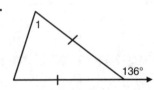

5. Use a two-column proof to show that $\overline{LM}$ bisects $\overline{DF}$.

   Given: $\overline{LF} \parallel \overline{DM}$, $\overline{DL} \parallel \overline{MF}$

   Prove: $\overline{LM}$ bisects $\overline{DF}$

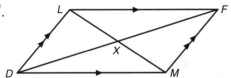

6

Assignment

Name _____ Date _____

Isosceles Triangle Theorems
Isosceles Triangle Base Theorem, Vertex Angle Theorem, Perpendicular Bisector Theorem, Altitude to Congruent Sides Theorem, and Angle Bisector to Congruent Sides Theorem

1. Use the Isosceles Triangle Perpendicular Bisector Theorem to make a statement about isosceles △CYX.

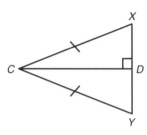

2. Use the Triangle Base Theorem to make a statement about isosceles △PBD.

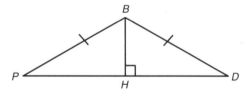

3. Use the Isosceles Triangle Angle Bisector to Congruent Sides Theorem to make a statement about isosceles △KSF.

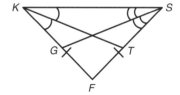

6

Solve for *x*.

4.

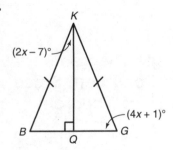

5.

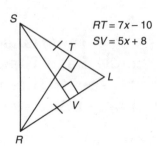

$RT = 7x - 10$

$SV = 5x + 8$

6.

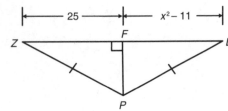

6

7. Use a flow chart proof to show that segment AY is congruent to segment CZ.

Given: $\overline{AB} \cong \overline{CB}$, $\angle AXY \cong \angle CXZ$

Prove: $\overline{AY} \cong \overline{CZ}$

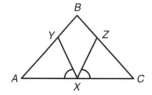

6

6

Assignment

Name _____ Date _____

Direct Proof vs. Indirect Proof
Inverse, Contrapositive, Direct Proof, and Indirect Proof

1. Consider the conditional statement "If a quadrilateral is a rectangle, then it is a parallelogram."

    a. Identify the hypothesis and the conclusion.

    b. Is the conditional statement true? Explain.

    c. Write the converse of the conditional statement. Is the converse true? Explain.

    d. Write the inverse of the conditional statement. Is the inverse true? Explain.

    e. Write the contrapositive of the conditional statement. Is the contrapositive true? Explain.

6

2. Consider the conditional statement "If a triangle is equilateral, then the triangle is equiangular."

a. Identify the hypothesis and the conclusion.

b. Is the conditional statement true? Explain.

c. Write the converse of the conditional statement. Is the converse true? Explain.

d. Write the inverse of the conditional statement. Is the inverse true? Explain.

e. Write the contrapositive of the conditional statement. Is the contrapositive true? Explain.

6

3. Use an indirect two-column proof to show that the complements of congruent angles are congruent.

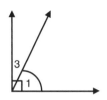 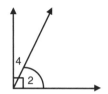

Given: $m\angle 1 = m\angle 2$, $m\angle 1 + m\angle 3 = 90°$, $m\angle 2 + m\angle 4 = 90°$

Prove: $m\angle 3 = m\angle 4$

4. Write an indirect paragraph proof to show that an isosceles triangle cannot have a base angle that is a right angle.

6

6

Assignment

Name _____ Date _____

Tangent Ratio
Tangent Ratio, Cotangent Ratio, and Inverse Tangent

Use the tangent ratio or the cotangent ratio to solve for *x*. Round each
answer to the nearest tenth.

1.

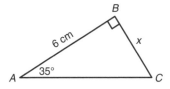

2.

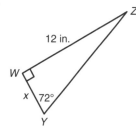

3.

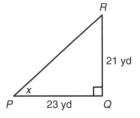

4.

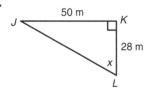

5. A roof truss is shown in the following figure. Use the figure to complete parts (a) through (d). Round each answer to the nearest hundredth.

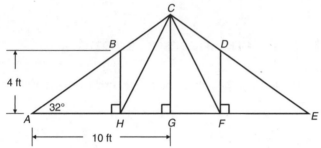

a. Use a tangent ratio to determine the height *CG* of the roof truss.

b. Use a cotangent ratio to determine *AH*.

c. Use a tangent ratio to determine the measure of angle *HCG*.

d. Use the Pythagorean Theorem to determine the length *CH* of the support beam.

7

Assignment

Name _____ Date _____

Sine Ratio
Sine Ratio, Cosecant Ratio, and Inverse Sine

Use the sine ratio or the cosecant ratio to solve for *x*. Round each answer to the nearest tenth.

1.

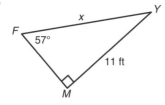

2.

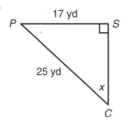

3.

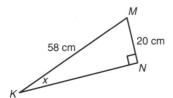

4.

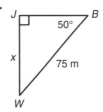

5. A roof truss is shown in the following figure. Use the figure to complete parts (a) through (d). Round each answer to the nearest hundredth.

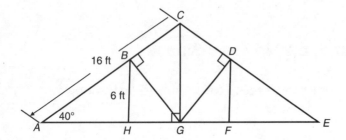

a. Use a sine ratio to determine the height *CG* of the roof truss.

b. Use a cosecant ratio to determine *AB*.

c. Use a sine ratio to determine the measure of angle *BGC*.

d. Use the Pythagorean Theorem to determine the length *BG* of the support beam.

7

Assignment

Name _____ Date _____

Cosine Ratio
Cosine Ratio, Secant Ratio, and Inverse Cosine

Use the cosine ratio or the secant ratio to solve for *x*. Round each answer to the nearest tenth.

1.

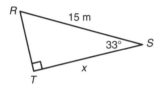

2.

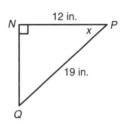

3.

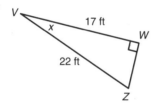

4.

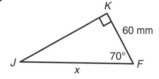

7

5. A bridge is shown in the following figure. Use the figure and the fact that triangle *AGC* is congruent to triangle *EGC* to complete parts (a) through (e). Round each answer to the nearest tenth.

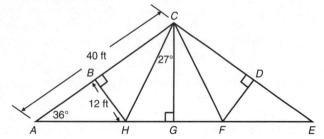

a. Use a cosine ratio to determine the width *AE* of the bridge.

b. Use the Pythagorean Theorem to determine the height *CG* of the bridge.

c. Use a secant ratio to determine *CH*.

7

d. Use a cosine ratio to determine the measure of angle *BHC*.

e. Does $\overline{CH}$ bisect angle *ACG*? Explain your reasoning.

7

Assignment

Name _____ Date _____

Angles of Elevation and Depression
Angles of Elevation, Angles of Depression, and Equivalent Trigonometric Ratios

1. An aircraft uses its radar to locate another aircraft that is 8000 feet away at a 12° angle of depression.

   a. Draw a figure to model this situation. Label the angle of depression and the hypotenuse. Label the side adjacent to the angle of depression as *x* and the side opposite the angle of depression as *y*.

   b. Calculate the vertical distance between the two aircraft. Round the distance to the nearest tenth.

   c. Calculate the horizontal distance between the two aircraft. Round the distance to the nearest tenth.

2. A pilot and co-pilot are performing a test run in a new airplane. The pilot is required to take off and fly in a straight path at an angle of elevation that is between 33 and 35 degrees until the plane reaches an altitude of 10,000 feet. When the plane reaches 10,000 feet, the co-pilot will take over.

a. Draw a figure to model this situation. Label the angle of elevation and the side opposite the angle of elevation. Label the side adjacent to the angle of elevation as x and the hypotenuse as y.

b. Determine the minimum and maximum horizontal distance between the point of take-off and the point at which the co-pilot takes over. Round each distance to the nearest tenth.

c. What is the minimum distance that the pilot flies the plane? What is the maximum distance that the pilot flies the plane? Round each distance to the nearest tenth.

7

Assignment

Name _____ Date _____

Squares and Rectangles
Properties of Squares and Rectangles

1. In quadrilateral *VWXY*, segments *VX* and *WY* bisect each other, and are perpendicular and congruent. Is this enough information to conclude that quadrilateral *VWXY* is a square? Explain.

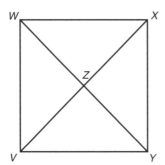

Quadrilateral *PQRS* is a rectangle with diagonals *PR* and *QS*.

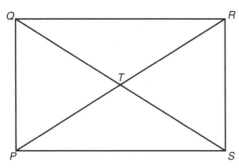

2. Name all parallel segments.

3. Name all congruent segments.

4. Name all right angles.

5. Name all congruent angles.

6. Name all congruent triangles.

Assignment

Name _____ Date _____

Parallelograms and Rhombi
Properties of Parallelograms and Rhombi

Quadrilateral *PLGM* is a parallelogram.

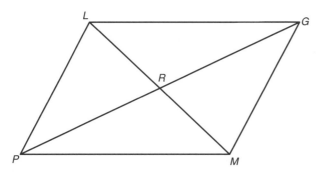

1. If $m\angle PLG = 124°$, what is $m\angle GMP$? Explain.

2. If $m\angle LPM = 56°$, what is $m\angle LGM$? Explain.

3. If the length of $\overline{LG}$ is 20 meters, what is *MP*? Explain.

4. If the length of $\overline{PR}$ is 12 inches, what is *GR*? Explain.

Quadrilateral *RHMB* is a rhombus.

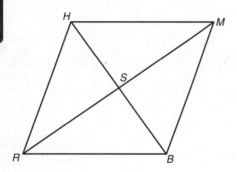

5. If $m\angle HRB = 70°$, what is $m\angle HMB$? Explain.

6. If $m\angle RHB = 55°$, what is $m\angle MHB$? Explain.

7. If the length of $\overline{RB}$ is 25 feet, what is HR? Explain.

8. If the length of $\overline{HS}$ is 18 centimeters, what is SB? Explain.

9. What is $m\angle RSB$? Explain.

Assignment

Name _____   Date _____

Kites and Trapezoids
Properties of Kites and Trapezoids

Quadrilateral *ABCD* is a kite.

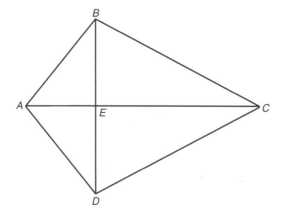

1. If $m\angle ABC = 95°$, what is $m\angle ADC$? Explain.

2. If $m\angle BCE = 34°$, what is $m\angle EBC$? Explain.

3. If the length of $\overline{AB}$ is 16 feet, what is AD? Explain.

4. If the length of $\overline{BD}$ is 25 feet, what is ED? Explain.

Quadrilateral *WXYZ* is an isosceles trapezoid.

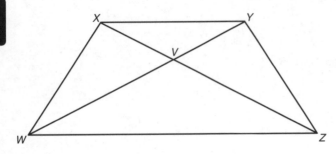

5. If $m\angle XWZ = 66°$, what is $m\angle YZW$? Explain.

6. If the length of $\overline{WY}$ is 10 inches, what is ZX? Explain.

7. If the length of $\overline{WX}$ is 7 inches, what is ZY? Explain.

Assignment

Name _____ Date _____

Decomposing Polygons
Sum of the Interior Angle Measures of a Polygon

Determine the measure of an interior angle of the given regular polygon.

1. regular nonagon

2. regular decagon

3. regular 15-gon

4. regular 47-gon

Determine the measure of the missing angle in each figure.

5.

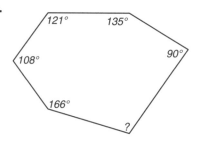

6.

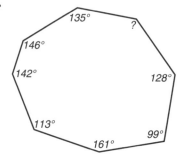

7. Use the figure to answer each question.

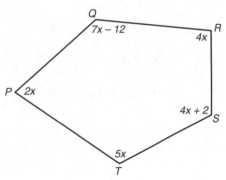

a. What is the sum of the measures of the interior angles of the polygon?

b. What is the value of x?

c. What is the measure of $\angle PTS$?

d. What is the measure of angle $\angle RQP$?

8. Suppose that the sum of the measures of the interior angles of a regular polygon is 157.5°. What type of polygon is it? Show your work and explain how you got your answer.

8

9. Suppose that the degree measure of each angle of a regular 12-gon can be represented by the expression $2x + 5$. Calculate the value of x.

8

Assignment

Name _____ Date _____

Exterior and Interior Angle Measurement Interactions
Sum of the Exterior Angle Measures of a Polygon

Use the figure below to answer each question.

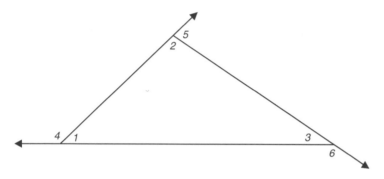

1. What is the sum of the measures of angles 1 and 4? Explain your reasoning.

2. What is the sum of the measures of angles 2 and 5? Explain your reasoning.

3. What is the sum of the measures of angles 3 and 6? Explain your reasoning.

4. What is the sum of the measures of angles 1, 2, 3, 4, 5, and 6? Explain your reasoning.

5. What is the sum of the measures of angles 1, 2, and 3? Explain your reasoning.

6. What is the difference of the sum of the measures of angles 1, 2, 3, 4, 5, and 6 and the sum of the measures of angles 1, 2, and 3? What does this demonstrate?

7. If a regular polygon has 30 sides, what is the measure of each exterior angle? Explain your reasoning.

8. The degree measure of each exterior angle of a regular octagon is represented by the expression $7x - 4$. Solve for x.

Assignment

Name _____ Date _____

Quadrilateral Family
Categorizing Quadrilaterals

List all types of quadrilaterals with the given characteristics.

1. The quadrilateral has four right angles.

2. The quadrilateral has four congruent sides.

3. Exactly one pair of opposite sides of the quadrilateral is parallel.

4. Exactly two pairs of opposite sides of the quadrilateral are parallel.

5. Opposite angles of the quadrilateral are congruent.

6. Exactly two pairs of adjacent sides are congruent.

7. The sum of the measures of the interior angles of the quadrilateral is 360°.

8. The sum of the measures of the exterior angles of the quadrilateral is 360°.

9. The diagonals of the quadrilateral are congruent.

10. The diagonals of the quadrilateral do not bisect each other.

11. Quadrilateral *ABCD* has congruent diagonals that are perpendicular to each other. What type of quadrilateral is *ABCD*?

12. Quadrilateral *JKLM* has consecutive vertex angles that are supplementary but not congruent. If the diagonals bisect the vertex angles, what type of quadrilateral is *JKLM*?

Assignment

Name _____   Date _____

Meeting Friends
The Distance Formula

Ben is playing soccer with his friends Abby and Clay. The grid shows their locations on the soccer field. Each grid square represents a square that is one meter long and one meter wide.

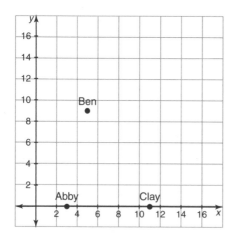

1. What are the coordinates of the location of each player?

2. How far does Abby have to kick the ball to reach Clay?

3. How far does Ben have to kick the ball to reach Abby?

4. How far does Ben have to kick the ball to reach Clay?

5. Graph and connect each pair of points on the grid below. Then calculate the distance between each pair of points.

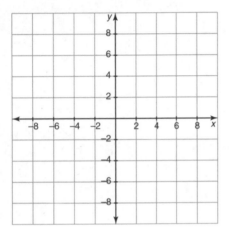

a. Points (−8, 3) and (−8, 9); Distance = _____

b. Points (−6, 8) and (−1, 8); Distance = _____

c. Points (8, −7) and (−4, −7); Distance = _____

d. Points (8, 8) and (8, −2); Distance = _____

6. Describe the method that you used to determine the distance between each pair of points in Question 5.

7. In Question 5, suppose that you were only given the coordinates of the points and did not graph them. Describe the method that you would use to calculate the distance between each pair of points.

9

8. Use the grid to graph and connect the given set of three points. Then, calculate the distances between the points.

a. (4, 1), (2, 1), and (4, 4)

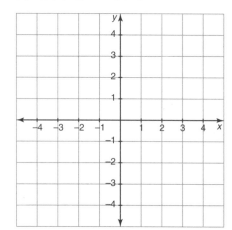

b. (1, −4), (1, 1), and (−2, −4)

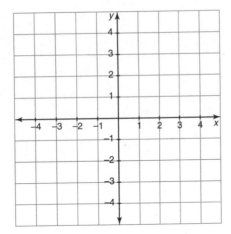

9. Describe the method that you used to calculate the distances between the points in Question 8.

10. Calculate the distance between each pair of points.

    a. (−37, −100) and (14, 0)

    Distance:

    b. (3, 9) and (4, 10)

    Distance:

    c. (−10, −7) and (13, 17)

    Distance:

Assignment

Name _____   Date _____

Treasure Hunt
The Midpoint Formula

The grid shows the locations of a sandbox and a water fountain in a park. Each grid square represents a square that is one meter long and one meter wide.

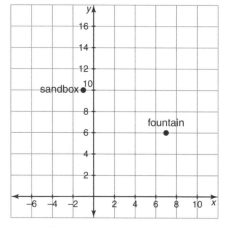

1. What are the coordinates of the locations of the sandbox and the water fountain?

2. Calculate the distance between the sandbox and the water fountain.

3. You decide to meet your friend halfway between the fountain and sandbox. Calculate the midpoint of the line segment that passes through the point representing the sandbox and the point representing the fountain.

The endpoints of a line segment are given. Use the Midpoint Formula to calculate the midpoint of each line segment.

4. $(-2, 5)$ and $(4, 1)$

5. $(4, 3)$ and $(-2, -5)$

6. $(-3, -4)$ and $(3, -6)$

7. If you know the midpoint of a line segment is $(2, 1)$, and one endpoint is $(3, -2)$, how can you calculate the other endpoint?

8. Calculate the midpoint of the line segment with endpoints $(-3, 8)$ and $(4, 1)$.

9. Explain how you can prove that your answer in Question 8 is the midpoint.

Assignment

Name _____ Date _____

Parking Lot Design
Parallel and Perpendicular Lines in the Coordinate Plane

The graphs of three lines are shown on the grid. Use this information to answer Questions 1 through 4.

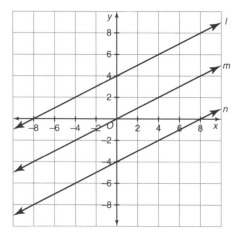

1. What is the slope of each line?

   a. Line *l*:

   b. Line *m*:

   c. Line *n*:

2. What is the *y*-intercept of each line?

   a. Line *l*:

   b. Line *m*:

   c. Line *n*:

3. Write the equation of each line in slope-intercept form.

   a. Line *l*:

   b. Line *m*:

   c. Line *n*:

4. Explain what the slopes and y-intercepts of lines l, m, and n tell you about the relationship between the lines.

5. Write an equation in slope-intercept form for a line that is parallel to the line given by $y = 2x - 6$ and that has each of the following characteristics.

a. 2 units above the given line

b. 8 units below the given line

c. passes through the point $(0, 8)$

d. passes through the point $(6, 0)$

6. Without graphing the lines, determine whether each pair of lines given by the equations are parallel. Show all your work.

a. $3x - y = 4$ and $2y - 6x = 12$

b. $2y = -8x + 10$ and $4x - y = -5$

The graphs of three lines are shown on the grid. Use this information to answer Questions 7 through 10.

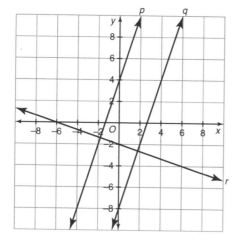

7. What is the slope of each line?

   a. Line p:

   b. Line q:

   c. Line r:

8. What is the y-intercept of each line?

   a. Line p:

   b. Line q:

   c. Line r:

9. Write the equation of each line in slope-intercept form.

   a. Line p:

   b. Line q:

   c. Line r:

10. Explain what the slopes and y-intercepts of lines p, q, and r tell you about the relationship between the lines.

11. Write an equation in slope-intercept form for the line that is perpendicular to the line given by each equation and that passes through the given point.

   a. $y = 2x + 4$; point (2, 0)

   b. $y = -x - 6$; point (3, 3)

12. Write equations for a horizontal line and a vertical line that pass through the point $(-3, 5)$.

13. Write an equation for the line that is perpendicular to the line given by $y = -2$ and that passes through the point (3, 4).

14. Write an equation for the line that is perpendicular to the line given by $x = 20$ and that passes through the point (3, 4).

15. The equation of line *l* on the grid below is $y = -2x - 4$. Point *D* is at (4, 3).

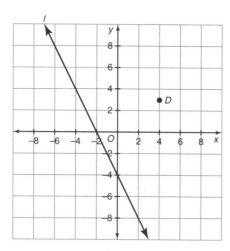

a. Draw the shortest line segment possible between point *D* and line *l* on the grid. Label the point where the segment and line *l* intersect point *C*.

b. Write an equation for the line that contains $\overline{CD}$.

c. Calculate the point of intersection of $\overline{CD}$ and line *l*.

d. Calculate the distance from point D to line l.

Assignment

Name _____   Date _____

Triangles in the Coordinate Plane
Midsegment of a Triangle

Triangle *FGH* has vertices *F*(−4, 2), *G*(4, 2), and *H*(4, −2). Triangle *FGH* is
inscribed in circle *O*.

9

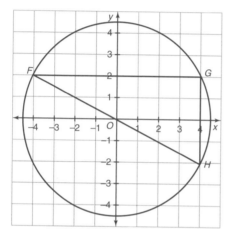

1. Calculate the slope of each side of triangle *FGH*.

   a. Slope of $\overline{FG}$:

   b. Slope of $\overline{GH}$:

   c. Slope of $\overline{FH}$:

2. Classify triangle *FGH* by its angles.

Triangle *ABC* has vertices at *A*(−2, 8), *B*(−8, −6), and *C*(4, −6).

3. Graph triangle *ABC* on the grid.

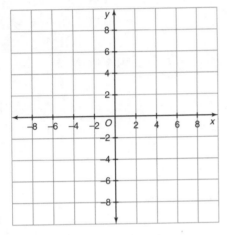

4. **a.** Classify triangle *ABC* by its side lengths.

   b. Verify the classification algebraically.

Triangle *PQR* has vertices at *P*(−1, 1), *Q*(4, −2), and *R*(−4, −2).

5. Graph triangle *PQR* on the grid below.

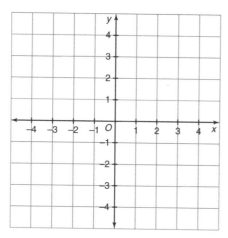

6. **a.** Classify triangle *PQR* by its side lengths.

b. Verify the classification algebraically.

7. In $\triangle XYZ$, the midpoint of $\overline{XY}$ is $A(-3, 0.5)$, the midpoint of $\overline{XZ}$ is $B(1, -6)$, and the midpoint of $\overline{YZ}$ is $C(3, 0.5)$. Use the Triangle Midsegment Theorem to determine the coordinates of the vertices of $\triangle XYZ$. Show all of your work and graph triangles ABC and XYZ on the grid.

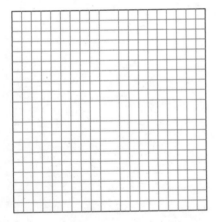

Assignment

Name _____   Date _____

What's the Point?
Points of Concurrency

Use a compass and straightedge to perform each construction.

1. Construct the incenter of △DEF.

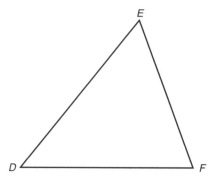

2. Construct the circumcenter of △ABC.

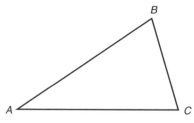

3. Construct the circumcenter of △DEF.

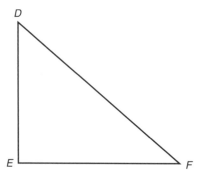

4. Construct the circumcenter of △GHI.

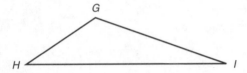

5. Construct the centroid of △ABC.

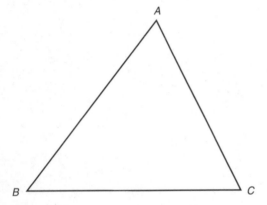

6. Construct the orthocenter of △JKL.

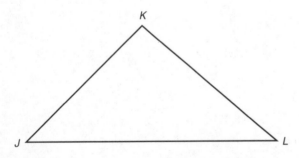

Name _____ Date _____

Write the term that best completes each statement.

7. The incenter of a triangle is the point of concurrency of the _____ of a triangle.

8. The circumcenter of a triangle is the point of concurrency of the _____ of a triangle.

9. The centroid of a triangle is the point of concurrency of the _____ of a triangle.

10. The orthocenter of a triangle is the point of concurrency of the _____ of a triangle.

Triangle *FGH* has vertices *F*(−4, 2), *G*(4, 2), and *H*(4, −2).

11. Use algebra to locate the centroid of △*FGH*.

12. Use algebra to locate the circumcenter of $\triangle FGH$.

9

Name _____ Date _____

Planning a Subdivision
Quadrilaterals in a Coordinate Plane

1. Quadrilateral *ABCD* has vertices *A*(−1, 6), *B*(3, 2), *C*(−1, −2), and *D*(−5, 2).

   a. Graph quadrilateral *ABCD*.

   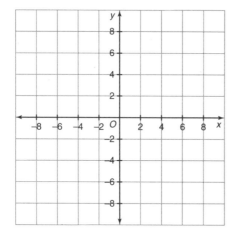

   b. Classify quadrilateral *ABCD* in as many ways as possible.

c. Prove your classification using algebra.

2. Quadrilateral *EFGH* has vertices *E*(−2, −1), *F*(−1, 2), *G*(5, 0), and *H*(4, −3).

a. Graph quadrilateral *EFGH*.

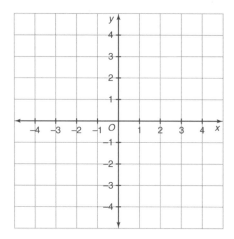

b. Classify quadrilateral *EFGH* in as many ways as possible.

c. Prove your classification using algebra.

3. Triangle *ABC* has vertices *A*(−1, 4), *B*(3, 0), and *C*(−3, −4), as shown on the grid.

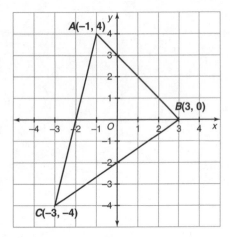

a. Determine and label point *D*, the midpoint of $\overline{AB}$:

b. Determine and label point *E*, the midpoint of $\overline{BC}$:

c. Determine and label point *F*, the midpoint of $\overline{AC}$:

d. Draw the midsegments of triangle *ABC*. Calculate the length of each side and midsegment of triangle *ABC*.

e. Classify quadrilateral *DECF,* formed by midsegments and segments of the triangles sides, in as many ways as possible.

f. Prove your classification using algebra.

g. Classify quadrilaterals *ADEF* and *DBEF.* Explain your classification.

4. Calculate the area of quadrilateral *DECF* from Question 3.

Assignment

Name _____   Date _____

Paper Snowflakes
Reflections

Use a compass and a protractor to reflect each line segment.

1. Reflect $\overline{AB}$ in line ℓ.

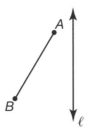

2. Reflect $\overline{CD}$ in line m.

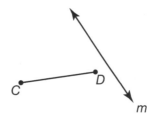

3. Reflect $\overline{EF}$ in line m.

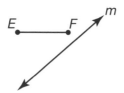

4. Use quadrilateral *ABCD* shown on the grid to complete parts (a) through (d).

a. On the grid, draw the image of quadrilateral *ABCD* reflected over the *y*-axis. Label the image *EFGH*.

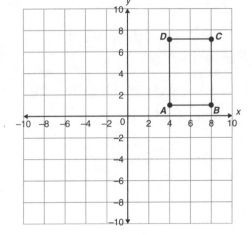

b. On the grid, draw the image of quadrilateral *ABCD* reflected over the *x*-axis. Label the image *JKLM*.

c. On the grid, draw the image of quadrilateral *ABCD* reflected over the line *y* = *x*. Label the image *PQRS*.

d. Identify the coordinates of quadrilaterals *EFGH*, *JKLM*, and *PQRS*.

5. The vertices of triangle *XYZ* are *X*(−5, −3), *Y*(−9, 4), and *Z*(2, 2). Without drawing the figure, determine the coordinates of the vertices of the image of triangle *XYZ* reflected over the *y*-axis. Explain your reasoning.

6. The vertices of trapezoid *ABCD* are *A*(−2, 3), *B*(−4, 7), *C*(4, 7), and *D*(2, 3).
Without drawing the figure, determine the coordinates of the vertices of the image
of trapezoid *ABCD* reflected over the *x*-axis. Explain your reasoning.

7. The vertices of pentagon *PQRST* are *P*(−2, −4), *Q*(−3, 0), *R*(2, 2), *S*(6, 0), and
T(2, −4). Without drawing the figure, determine the coordinates of the vertices of
the image of pentagon *PQRST* reflected over the line *y* = *x*. Explain your reasoning.

10

Assignment

Name _____ Date _____

Good Lighting
Rotations

Use a compass and a protractor to rotate each line segment.

1. If a preimage point (x, y) is reflected in the _____, then its image point is $(x, -y)$.

2. If a preimage point is reflected in the y-axis, then its image point is _____.

3. Use $\triangle ABC$ shown on the grid to complete parts (a) through (d).

   a. Draw the image of $\triangle ABC$ after it is rotated 90° counterclockwise about the origin. Draw the image on the same grid as $\triangle ABC$ and label it $\triangle FGH$.

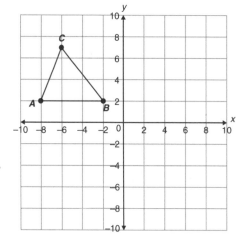

   b. Draw the image of $\triangle ABC$ after it is rotated 180° about the origin. Draw the image on the same grid as $\triangle ABC$ and label it $\triangle RST$.

   c. Draw the image of $\triangle ABC$ after it is rotated 90° clockwise about the origin. Draw the image on the same grid as $\triangle ABC$ and label it $\triangle XYZ$.

   d. Identify the coordinates of triangles FGH, RST, and XYZ.

4. The vertices of parallelogram *ABCD* are *A*(−10, 0), *B*(−8, 4), *C*(−4, −2), and *D*(−6, −6). Without drawing the figure, determine the coordinates of the vertices of the image of quadrilateral *ABCD* after it is rotated 180° about the origin. Explain your reasoning.

5. The vertices of triangle *JKL* are *J*(−4, −3), *K*(1, 5), and *L*(1, −6). Without drawing the figure, determine the coordinates of the vertices of the image of triangle *JKL* after it is rotated 90° clockwise about the origin. Explain your reasoning.

10

6. The vertices of hexagon *NPQRST* are *N*(0, −4), *P*(−1, −2), *Q*(0, 0), *R*(3, 2), *S*(6, −1), and *T*(4, −4). Without drawing the figure, determine the coordinates of the vertices of the image of hexagon *NPQRST* after it is rotated 90° counterclockwise about the origin. Explain your reasoning.

Assignment

Name _____   Date _____

Web Page Design
Translations

1. Use triangle *ABC* shown on the grid to complete parts (a) through (d).

   a. On the grid, draw the image of
   triangle *ABC* translated 6 units to
   the right. Label the image *DEF*.

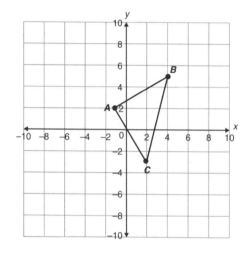

   b. On the gird, draw the image of
   triangle *ABC* translated 5 units down.
   Label the image *LMN*.

   c. On the grid, draw the image of
   triangle *ABC* translated 8 units to the
   left and 3 units up. Label the image *VWX*.

   d. Identify the coordinates of
   triangles *DEF*, *LMN*, and *VWX*.

2. The vertices of quadrilateral *ABCD* are *A*(−2, −1), *B*(0, 5), *C*(4, 7), and *D*(3, −1). Without drawing the figure, determine the coordinates of the vertices of the image of quadrilateral *ABCD* translated 4 units to the right and 10 units up. Explain your reasoning.

3. The vertices of pentagon *VWXYZ* are *V*(−5, 0), *W*(−2, 2), *X*(2, 3), *Y*(4, 1), and *Z*(−1, −3). Without drawing the figure, determine the coordinates of the vertices of the image of pentagon *VWXYZ* translated 7 units to the left and 2 units down. Explain your reasoning.

4. The vertices of triangle *PQR* are *P*(−7, 2), *Q*(−6, 6), and *R*(−5, 3). Without drawing the figure, determine the coordinates of the vertices of the image of triangle *PQR* translated 8 units to the right and 5 units down. Explain your reasoning.

5. Use pentagon *ABCDE* shown on the grid to complete parts (a) through (c).

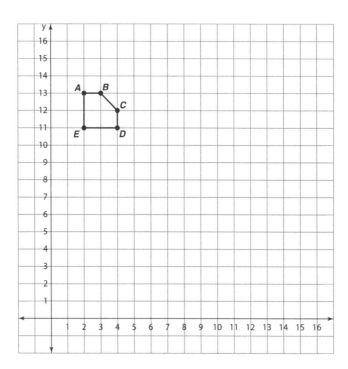

a. On the grid, draw the image of pentagon *ABCDE* using the transformation
$(x, y) \rightarrow (x, y - 10)$. Label the image *A′B′C′D′E′*.

b. What kind of transformation did you perform in part (a)?

c. Determine two parallel lines over which the pentagon can be reflected so that it
has the same coordinates as pentagon *A′B′C′D′E′* from part (a).

10

Assignment

Name _____   Date _____

Shadow Puppets
Dilations

1. Use quadrilateral *ABCD* shown on the grid to complete parts (a) through (c).

   a. On the grid, draw the image of quadrilateral *ABCD* dilated using a scale factor of 3 with the center of dilation at the origin. Label the image *JKLM*.

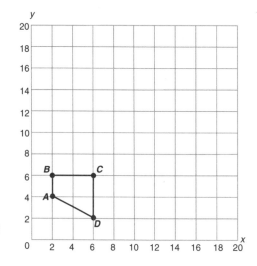

   b. On the grid, draw the image of quadrilateral *ABCD* dilated using a scale factor of 0.5 with the center of dilation at the origin. Label the image *WXYZ*.

   c. Identify the coordinates of quadrilaterals *JKLM* and *WXYZ*.

2. The vertices of triangle *ABC* are *A*(−6, 15), *B*(0, 5), and *C*(3, 10). Without drawing the figure, determine the coordinates of the vertices of the image of triangle *ABC* dilated using a scale factor of $\frac{1}{3}$ with the center of dilation at the origin. Explain your reasoning.

3. The vertices of trapezoid *WXYZ* are *W*(−1, 2), *X*(−3, −1), *Y*(5, −1), and *Z*(3, 2). Without drawing the figure, determine the coordinates of the vertices of the image of trapezoid *WXYZ* dilated using a scale factor of 5 with the center of dilation at the origin. Explain your reasoning.

4. The vertices of hexagon *PQRSTV* are *P*(−5, 0), *Q*(−5, 5), *R*(0, 7), *S*(5, 2), *T*(5, −2), and *V*(0, −5). Without drawing the figure, determine the coordinates of the vertices of the image of hexagon *PQRSTV* dilated about the origin using a scale factor of 4.2. Explain your reasoning.

5. Triangle *A′B′C′* is a dilation of △*ABC* with the center of dilation at the origin. List the coordinates of the vertices of △*ABC* and △*A′B′C′*. What is the scale factor of the dilation? Explain.

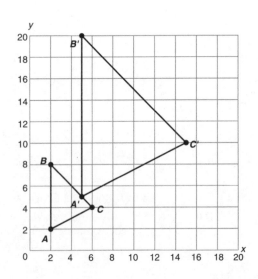

6. On the grid, draw the image of quadrilateral *QRST* using the dilation
   $(x, y) \rightarrow (0.75x, 0.75y)$. Label the image *Q'R'S'T'*.

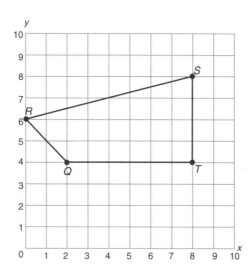

Assignment

Name _____ Date _____

Cookie Cutters and the Alphabet
Symmetry

Determine whether each figure has line symmetry. If it does, sketch the line(s) of symmetry. Then determine whether each figure has rotational symmetry. If it does, describe the rotational symmetry.

1.

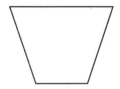

2.

3.

4.

5.

6.

Complete each figure given its line of symmetry.

7. The line of symmetry is the *y*-axis.

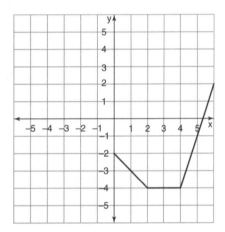

8. The line of symmetry is the *x*-axis.

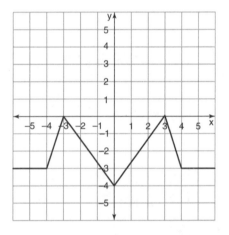

9. The line of symmetry is *y* = *x*.

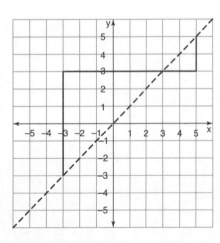

10. Complete the Venn diagram for the following mathematical symbols.

Perpendicular symbol: ⊥   Square root symbol: √

Percent symbol: %   Equals sign: =

Plus sign: +   Division sign: ÷

Multiplication sign: ×   Angle symbol: ∠

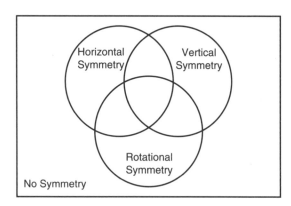

Assignment

Name _____ Date _____

Koch Snowflake and Tessellations
Fractals and Tessellations

1. In class, you investigated a famous fractal called the Koch Snowflake.
   There are many other fractals that are interesting to study. One of them is called
   the Sierpinski Triangle. To create the first three stages of the Sierpinski Triangle,
   use the figure and follow the steps below.

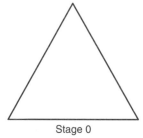
Stage 0

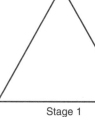
Stage 1

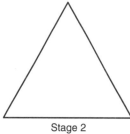
Stage 2

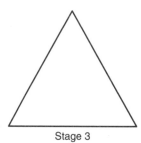
Stage 3

   a. Estimate the midpoint of each side of the triangle in Stage 1. Connect the
      midpoints within the triangle to form another triangle. Shade the new triangle.
      You have completed Stage 1.

   b. Copy the triangle from Stage 1 into the triangle in Stage 2. Estimate the
      midpoint of each side of each unshaded triangle formed in Stage 2.
      Connect the midpoints within the unshaded triangles. Shade the new triangles.
      You have completed Stage 2.

c. In Stage 3, continue this pattern.

d. Use Stage 0 through Stage 3 of the fractal you created to complete the table.

Stage	Number of Unshaded Triangles
0	
1	
2	
3	

e. Predict the number of unshaded triangles in Stage 4 and Stage 5. Record your results in the table in part (d).

f. Predict the number of unshaded triangles in Stage n. Record your results in the table in part (d).

2. Create your own tessellation using only isosceles right triangles and isosceles trapezoids.

Assignment

Name _____ Date _____

Riding a Ferris Wheel
Introduction to Circles

Circle *C* is shown. Identify the indicated components of circle *C*.

1. Name the diameter(s).

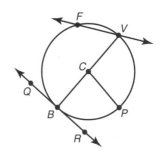

2. Name the radius(radii).

3. Name the chord(s).

4. Name the tangent(s).

5. Name the secant(s).

6. Name the central angle(s).

7. Name the inscribed angle(s).

8. Name the major arc(s).

11

9. Name the minor arc(s).

10. Name the semicircle(s).

Draw the indicated part using each given circle.

11. Draw chord *ST* using circle *C*.

12. Draw tangent *BC* using circle *S*, where *B* is the point of tangency.

13. Draw secant *LM* using circle *P*.

14. Draw central angle *XYZ* using circle *Y*.

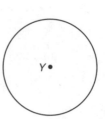

15. Draw inscribed angle *JKL* using circle *D*.

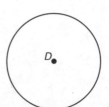

Assignment

Name _____ Date _____

Holding the Wheel
Central Angles, Inscribed Angles, and Intercepted Arcs

Use circle S to answer each question. Explain your reasoning.

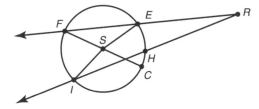

1. Suppose that $m\widehat{CE} = 59°$. What is $m\widehat{CFE}$?

2. Suppose that $m\angle CSI = 124°$. What is $m\widehat{FI}$?

3. Suppose that $m\widehat{CE} = 55°$. What is $m\angle EFC$?

4. Suppose that $m\angle FSI = 71°$. What is $m\widehat{IC}$?

5. In circle E shown, $m\angle ANG = 74°$.

a. Determine $m\angle AEG$.

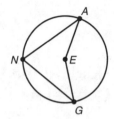

b. Determine $m\widehat{ANG}$.

6. In circle H shown, $m\widehat{CA} = 105°$, $m\widehat{EA} = 47°$, and $m\widehat{ET} = 100°$.

a. Determine $m\angle ETC$.

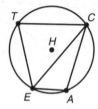

b. Determine $m\angle TCE$.

c. Determine $m\angle CAE$.

d. Determine $m\angle TEA$.

Assignment

Name _____   Date _____

Manhole Covers
Measuring Angles Inside and Outside of Circles

1. In circle P shown, $m\widehat{DE} = 75°$ and $m\widehat{NA} = 49°$. Determine $m\angle DTE$.

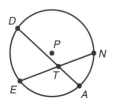

2. In circle K shown, $m\widehat{DN} = 144°$ and $m\angle NCA = 68°$. Determine $m\widehat{EA}$.

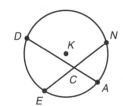

3. In circle O shown, m$\widehat{SN}$ = 55° and m$\widehat{HA}$ = 35°. Determine $m\angle SCH$.

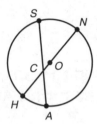

4. In circle X shown, $m\widehat{AS}$ = 11° and $m\widehat{MS}$ = 104°. Determine $m\angle DCM$.

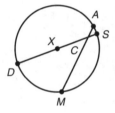

5. In circle *S* shown, $m\widehat{ER} = 38°$ and $m\widehat{OT} = 121°$. Determine $m\angle OUT$.

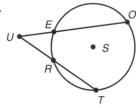

6. In circle *M* shown, $\overline{XE}$ is a diameter of the circle and $m\widehat{XT} = 132°$.
Draw a chord that connects points *X* and *T*. Then determine $m\angle XUT$.

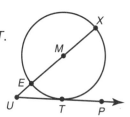

7. In circle G shown, $OH = ES$, $m\widehat{OH} = 41°$, and $m\widehat{HE} = 171°$. Determine $m\angle EUH$.

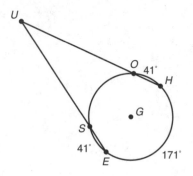

8. In circle B shown, $m\widehat{HE} = 99°$. Determine $m\angle HUE$.

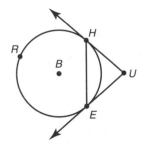

9. In circle T shown, $m\angle RCE = 57°$ and $m\widehat{RE} = 141°$. Determine $m\widehat{BL}$.

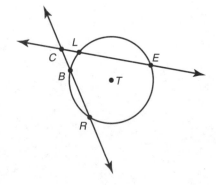

Assignment

Name _____ Date _____

Color Theory
Chords

1. Use circle *T* to complete parts (a) through (g).

   a. Draw an inscribed right angle in circle *T*. Label each point where the angle intersects the circle. What is the name of the right angle?

   b. Draw the chord determined by the inscribed right angle. What is the name of the chord?

   c. What else do you know about the chord determined by an inscribed right angle?

   d. Draw a second inscribed right angle in circle *T*. Label each point where the angle intersects the circle. What is the name of the second right angle?

   e. Draw the chord determined by the second inscribed right angle. What is the name of the chord?

   f. What else do you know about the chord determined by the second inscribed right angle?

g. Do you think every inscribed right angle will determine the longest chord of the circle, which is the diameter of the circle? Explain your reasoning.

2. The figure shows a section of a circle. Draw two chords and construct their perpendicular bisectors to locate the center of the circle.

3. In circle *G* shown below, *MG* = 1.84 centimeters, *GL* = 1.98 centimeters, *m∠GLH* = 90°, and *m∠GMK* = 90°. Determine which chord is longer, *IH* or *JK*. Explain your reasoning.

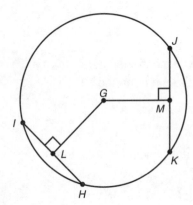

Assignment

Name _____ Date _____

Solar Eclipses
Tangents and Secants

1. Use circle O to complete parts (a) through (h).

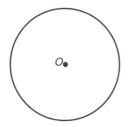

a. Draw a tangent to circle O. Label the point of tangency as point A.

b. Label another point on the tangent you drew in part (a) as point B.

c. Draw a second tangent line to circle O that passes through point B. Label this second point of tangency as point C.

d. Draw the radii $\overline{OA}$ and $\overline{OC}$.

e. What is $m\angle OAB$? Explain your reasoning.

f. What is $m\angle OCB$? Explain your reasoning.

11

g. Use a protractor to determine the measure of ∠AOC.

h. What is m∠ABC? Explain your reasoning.

2. In the figure shown, rays *LJ* and *LH* are tangent to circle *K*, and the measure of angle *LJH* is 71°. What is the measure of angle *JLH*? Explain your reasoning.

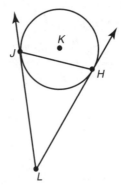

3. In the figure shown, *WV* = 36 inches, point *X* is a midpoint of segment *WV*, and *YV* = 40 inches. What is *YZ*? Explain your reasoning.

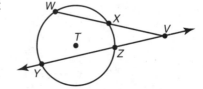

4. In the figure shown, line *FG* is tangent to circle *Q*, *BC* = 10 feet, and *CG* = 4 feet. What is *FG*? Explain your reasoning.

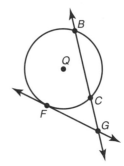

© 2010 Carnegie Learning, Inc.

214   Chapter 11 ● Assignments

Assignment

Name _____ Date _____

Replacement for a Carpenter's Square
Inscribed and Circumscribed Triangles and Quadrilaterals

1. In the figure shown, △ABC is inscribed in circle D and $m\angle A = 55°$.
   What is $m\angle C$? Explain your reasoning.

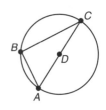

2. In the figure shown, △XYZ is inscribed in circle W and $XY = YZ$.
   What is $m\angle X$? Explain your reasoning.

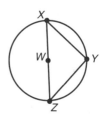

3. In the figure shown, △RST is inscribed in circle Q, $RS = 18$ centimeters,
   and $ST = 24$ centimeters. What is RT? Explain your reasoning.

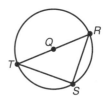

4. In the figure shown, quadrilateral *FGHJ* is inscribed in circle *K*,
    $m\angle F = 112°$, and $m\angle G = 87°$. What are $m\angle H$ and $m\angle J$?
    Explain your reasoning.

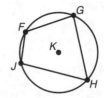

11

5. In the figure shown, quadrilateral *LMNP* is inscribed in circle *R*,
    $m\angle P = 57°$, and $m\angle L = m\angle N$. What are $m\angle M$, $m\angle L$, and $m\angle N$?
    Explain your reasoning.

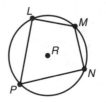

Assignment

Name _____   Date _____

Gears
Arc Length

1. In circle *A* shown describe the difference between the measure of minor arc *BC* and the length of minor arc *BC*. Use complete sentences in your answer.

    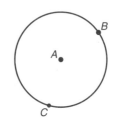

2. In circle *E* shown, the radius of the circle is 16 centimeters and $m\angle JSB$ is 40°. Determine the arc length of $\overset{\frown}{JB}$. Use complete sentences in your answer.

    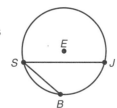

3. In circle *I* shown, the radius is 6 millimeters and $m\overset{\frown}{HC}$ is 80°.
Determine the arc length of $\overset{\frown}{SC}$. Use complete sentences
in your answer.

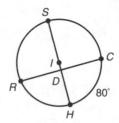

4. In circle *H* shown, the arc length of $\overset{\frown}{SJ}$ is 24π centimeters
and $m\angle JOS$ is 80°. Determine the length of a diameter of
circle *H*. Use complete sentences in your answer.

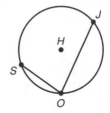

Assignment

Name _____   Date _____

Playing Darts
Sectors and Segments of a Circle

In circle *C* shown, △*ABC* is an equilateral triangle and *AC* = 10 inches.

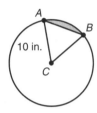

1. Calculate the area of sector *ACB*. Express your answer in terms of π and as a decimal rounded to the nearest hundredth.

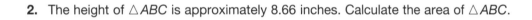

2. The height of △*ABC* is approximately 8.66 inches. Calculate the area of △*ABC*.

3. Calculate the area of segment *AB* of circle *C*. Express your answer in terms of π and as a decimal rounded to the nearest hundredth.

In circle _A_ shown, the radius is 18 centimeters and △_ABC_ is an equilateral triangle.

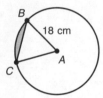

4. Calculate the area of the sector of circle _A_ that is bounded by radii _AB_ and _AC_. Express your answer in terms of π and as a decimal rounded to the nearest hundredth.

5. Calculate the area of the segment of circle _A_ that is bounded by chord _BC_. Express your answer in terms of π and as a decimal rounded to the nearest hundredth.

In circle *S* shown, the radius is 22 feet and *m∠RST* = 90°.

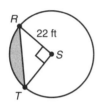

6. Calculate the area of the sector of circle *S* that is bounded by radii *SR* and *ST*. Express your answer in terms of π and as a decimal rounded to the nearest hundredth.

7. Calculate the area of the segment of circle *S* that is bounded by chord *RT*. Express your answer in terms of π and as a decimal rounded to the nearest hundredth.

11

11

Assignment

Name _____ Date _____

The Coordinate Plane
Circles and Polygons on the Coordinate Plane

1. In circle *C* shown, chords *AB* and *DE* intersect at point *F*. Show that the product of the lengths of the segments of chord *AB* is equal to the product of the lengths of the segments of chord *DE*. Then determine the theorem that is illustrated. Show all your work.

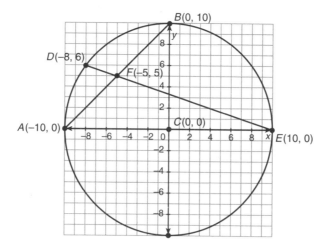

11

2. Triangle *JKL* is inscribed in circle *D*. Show that △*JKL* is an isosceles right triangle. Show all your work.

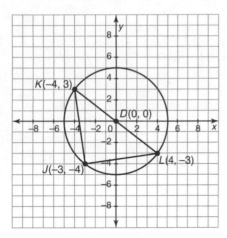

3. Quadrilateral *WXYZ* is a kite. Draw the quadrilateral formed by connecting the midpoints of the sides of the kite and label this quadrilateral *ABCD*. Then classify quadrilateral *ABCD*. Show all your work.

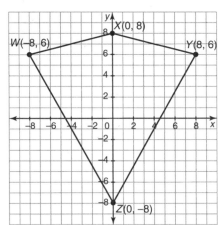

11

Assignment

Name _____ Date _____

Box It Up
Nets and Platonic Solids

Determine whether each solid is a polyhedron. Explain your reasoning.

1.

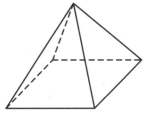

2.

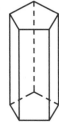

3.

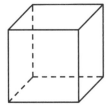

4.

5. Use the polyhedron shown to complete parts (a) through (e).

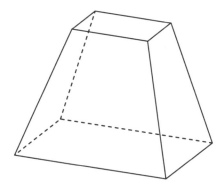

12

a. Determine the number of vertices of the polyhedron.

b. Determine the number of faces of the polyhedron.

c. Determine the number of edges of the polyhedron.

d. Describe the polygons used to create the polyhedron.

e. Is the polyhedron a regular polyhedron? Explain why or why not.

6. Create a net for a tetrahedron on the grid shown.

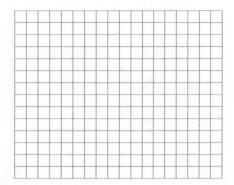

7. Describe the polyhedron that is represented by the net shown with respect to vertices, faces, edges, and overall shape.

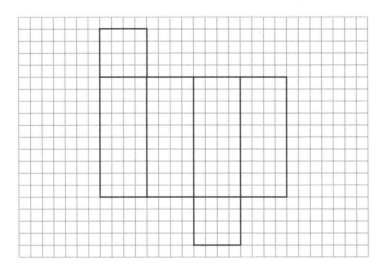

8. Describe the polyhedron that is represented by the net shown with respect to vertices, faces, edges, and overall shape.

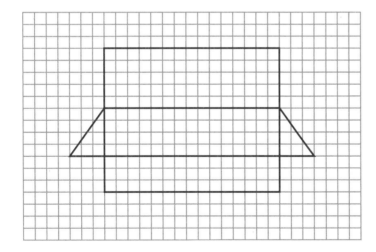

12

Assignment

Name _____ Date _____

Backyard Barbecue
Introduction to Volume and Surface Area

1. You want to build a rectangular storage box to hold barbecue supplies for your new patio.

    a. How many measurements are involved in building the storage box? Describe these measurements.

    b. You want the box to have a rectangular base with a length of 5 feet and a width of 3.5 feet. You want the box to be 2 feet tall. Sketch a model of the storage box and label the measurements.

    c. You are going to cover the outside of the storage box with a special rainproof coating. What is the area that you will be covering?

12

d. You are going to cover the top and sides of the storage box with 12-inch by 12-inch tiles. The tiles are sold in boxes of 20. How many boxes of tiles will you need to purchase? Explain your reasoning.

e. How much space is inside of the storage box?

Name _____   Date _____

Calculate the surface area of each figure.

2.

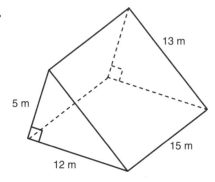

3.

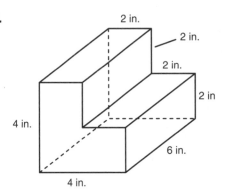

Calculate the volume of each figure.

4.

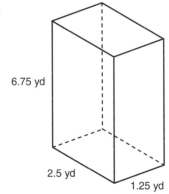

5.

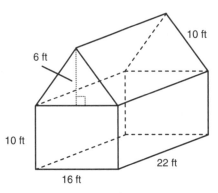

12

Assignment

Name _____ Date _____

Turn Up the Volume and Let's Bend Light Beams
Volume and Surface Area of a Prism

Name each prism.

1.

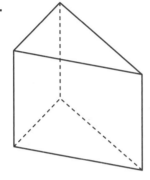

2.

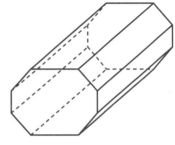

Create a sketch of each prism.

3. Pentagonal prism

4. Right triangular prism

12

5. You want to build a storage shed in your back yard for your lawn equipment. Two designs for the shed are shown below.

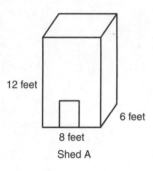

12 feet

6 feet

8 feet

Shed A

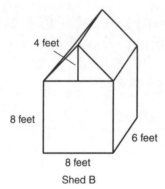

4 feet

8 feet

6 feet

8 feet

Shed B

a. What is the volume of Shed A?

b. What is the volume of Shed B?

c. Suppose that you want to build a shed that gives you the most space inside. Which shed should you choose?

Name _____ Date _____

6. You are designing a box in the shape of a rectangular prism for a shipping company. The box must have a volume of 24 cubic feet.

a. Complete the table with possible whole number dimensions for the box and calculate the corresponding surface areas.

Length (ft)	Width (ft)	Height (ft)	Volume (ft³)	Surface Area (ft²)
			24	
			24	
			24	
			24	
			24	
			24	

b. What are the dimensions of the box with the greatest surface area?

c. What are the dimensions of the box with the smallest surface area?

d. Which box do you think the shipping company would prefer? Explain your reasoning.

Assignment

Name _____ Date _____

Modern-Day Pyramids and Soundproofing
Volume and Surface Area of a Pyramid

Name each pyramid.

1.

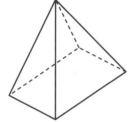

2.

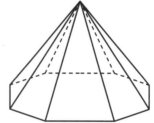

Create a sketch of each pyramid.

3. Right triangular pyramid

4. Hexagonal pyramid

5. The Luxor Hotel in Las Vegas is a replica of Khafre Pyramid at Giza, one of the seven wonders of the world. The Luxor's base is a square with a side length of 646 feet, and it is 350 feet tall.

   a. What is the volume of the Luxor Hotel?

b. The Khafre Pyramid has a volume of 2,226,450 cubic meters. Its base is a square with a side length of 215 meters. What is the height of the Khafre Pyramid?

6. A store sells square pyramid-shaped scented candles. The dimensions of two of the candles are shown below.

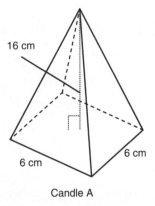

Candle A

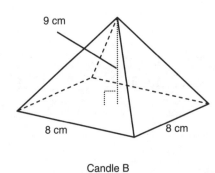

Candle B

a. Calculate the slant height of each candle.

b. Calculate the surface area of each candle.

12

c. Calculate the volume of each candle.

d. Both candles are made of wax. Which candle contains more wax? Explain.

e. Both candles are sold in a plastic wrapping. Which candle requires more plastic wrapping? Explain.

12

12

Assignment

Name _____ Date _____

Making Concrete Stronger
Volume and Surface Area of a Cylinder

Calculate the surface area of each cylinder. Use 3.14 for π and round to the nearest tenth, if necessary.

1.

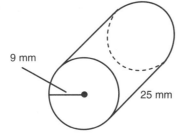

9 mm

25 mm

2.

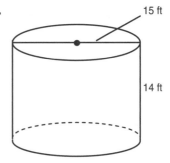

15 ft

14 ft

Calculate the volume of each cylinder. Use 3.14 for π and round to the nearest tenth, if necessary.

3.

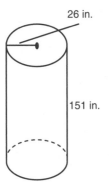

26 in.

151 in.

4.

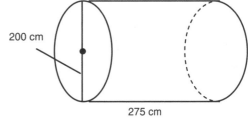

200 cm

275 cm

12

5. A tunnel through a mountain is in the shape of half of a cylinder. The entrance to the tunnel is 40 feet wide, as shown. The tunnel is 800 feet long.

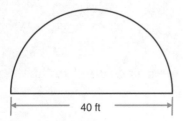

40 ft

a. How much of the mountain had to be displaced to build the tunnel?

b. The inside of the tunnel is lined with cement, which includes the arc of the tunnel and the road. How much cement was used?

12

6. Your municipality is replacing the storage tanks in the community. In which plan is the total capacity greater?

Plan 1: Install one cylindrical tank that is 150 feet tall and has a radius of 50 feet.

Plan 2: Install two cylindrical tanks that are 75 feet tall. One cylindrical tank has a radius of 30 feet and one tank has a radius of 25 feet.

Use 3.14 for π and round your answers to the nearest tenth if necessary.

12

12

Assignment

Name _____ Date _____

Sand Piles
Volume and Surface Area of a Cone

Calculate the volume of each cone described. Use 3.14 for π and round to the nearest tenth, if necessary.

1. A traffic cone has a radius of 9 inches and a height of 30 inches.

2. A funnel that is used to change the oil in a car is in the shape of a cone. The base of the funnel has a circumference of 60 centimeters. The height of the funnel is 25 centimeters.

3. A mini ice cream cone has a diameter of 3.5 centimeters and a height of 6 centimeters.

4. A cone has a radius of 6 meters and a height of 8 meters. Use this information to complete parts (a) through (c). Use 3.14 for π and round to the nearest tenth, if necessary.

   a. Draw a sketch of the cone and label its measurements.

   b. Calculate the slant height of the cone.

   c. Calculate the surface area of the cone.

Name _____ Date _____

Use the given information to calculate the missing measures for each cone. Write your answers in terms of π. Show all your work.

5. Height =

Radius = 5 ft

Slant height =

Surface area =

Volume = 100π ft³

6. Height = 39 yd

Radius =

Slant height = 65 yd

Surface area =

Volume =

12

12

Assignment

Name _____ Date _____

Walk in the Footsteps of Archimedes
Volume and Surface Area of a Sphere

Calculate the surface area of each sphere. Use 3.14 for π and round to the nearest tenth, if necessary.

1.

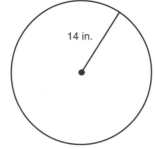

14 in.

2.

2.5 cm

Calculate the volume of each sphere. Use 3.14 for π and round to the nearest tenth, if necessary.

3.

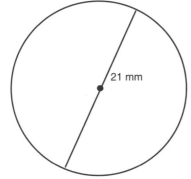

21 mm

4.

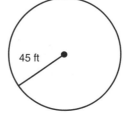

45 ft

12

5. A can holds 3 tennis balls as shown in the figure. The radius of each tennis ball is 3 centimeters.

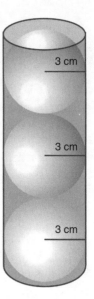

  a. What is the volume of a single tennis ball?

  b. What is the total volume all 3 tennis balls take up?

  c. Can you determine the height of the can? Explain your reasoning.

  d. What is the volume of the can? Use 3.14 for π.

  e. What is the volume of the can not taken up by the tennis balls?

6. A new umbrella design was created in the shape of a hemisphere with a special plastic coating on the material to better repel water. The diameter of the umbrella is about 1 yard. Because the umbrella is still in its beginning stages, the manufacturer only produces 200 of them to be sold in select markets. How much of the specially coated material must be produced for the manufacture of these umbrellas?

Assignment

Name _____ Date _____

Tree Rings
Cross Sections

Describe the shape of each cross section.

Describe the shape of each cross section.

1.

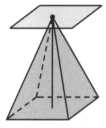

2.

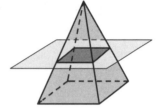

3.

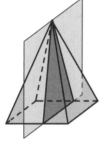

4.

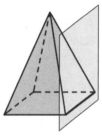

5.

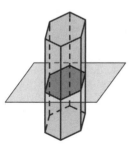

6.

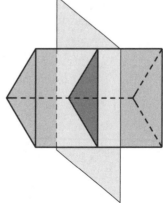

13

7. Sketch two cross sections of a pentagonal prism – one cross section that is parallel to a base and another cross section that is perpendicular to a base.

8. Sketch two cross sections of a cone – one cross section that is parallel to a base and another cross section that is perpendicular to a base.

9. A solid's cross section parallel to a base is an octagon. A cross section of the solid perpendicular to a base is a triangle. Identify the solid.

10. A solid's cross section parallel to a base is a triangle. A cross section of the solid perpendicular to a base is a rectangle. Identify the solid.

Assignment

Name _____ Date _____

Minerals and Crystals
Euler's Formula and Euler's Theorems

Determine the missing information using Euler's Formula. Show your work.

1. A solid has 8 faces and 12 vertices. How many edges does it have?

2. A solid has 7 faces and 12 edges. How many vertices does it have?

3. A solid has 5 vertices and 8 edges. How many faces does it have?

4. A solid has 7 faces and 15 edges. How many vertices does it have?

13

5. A small college has five buildings on its campus. Walkways connect the five buildings, as shown in the diagram.

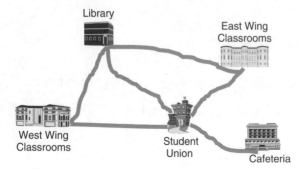

a. Draw a vertex-edge graph to represent the campus. Use the first letter of each building to represent the nodes. Label the edges with numbers.

b. Use your graph in part (a) to name the path that goes from the library to the west wing classrooms to the student union.

c. Use your graph in part (a) to name the path that goes from the cafeteria to the student union to the library to the east wing classrooms.

13

d. Identify all of the odd vertices.

e. Identify all of the even vertices.

f. Is this network traversable? Why or why not?

g. Does this network have an Euler path? If so, name one. If not, explain why not.

13

13

Assignment

Name _____   Date _____

Edges and Ends
Vertex-Edge Graphs

Name each prism.

1. Six friends live in the same housing plan. The friends made bicycle paths to each other's homes. The map shows the locations of their homes and the bicycle paths that they created. The bicycle paths are numbered.

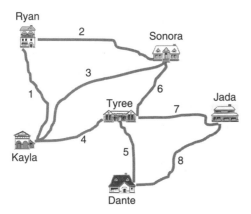

   a. Draw a vertex-edge graph to represent this problem.

   b. How do you know that this network contains at least one Euler path?

13

c. Determine an Euler path for this network, beginning at Kayla's house.

d. Determine an Euler path for this network, beginning at Tyree's house.

e. The housing plan committee has decided to hire paving contractors to pave the bicycle paths. The committee wants the contractors to choose a route so that they travel each path exactly once. Is this possible? If so, describe the route. If not, explain why not.

2. A spy network consists of one supervisor, S; three handlers, H_1, H_2, and H_3; and seven assets, A_1, A_2, A_3, A_4, A_5, A_6, and A_7. Assets A_1 and A_2 report to H_1. Assets A_3 and A_4 report to H_2. Assets A_5 and A_6 report to H_3. Asset A_7 reports directly to the supervisor. All three handlers report to the supervisor, and H_1 and H_2 also report any information either receives to each other.

a. Create a digraph D to represent the situation. Label the arcs.

b. Define the set of vertices of the digraph.

© 2010 Carnegie Learning, Inc.

13

c. Define the set of edges of the digraph.

d. Define each edge of the digraph as an ordered pair.

e. Is the digraph a simple digraph? Explain.

3. Digraph M is defined as:

$M(V) = \{W, X, Y, Z\}$

$M(E) = \{a_1, a_2, a_3, a_4, a_5, a_6\}$

$a_1 = (X, W), a_2 = (W, X), a_3 = (X, Z), a_4 = (X, Y), a_5 = (W, Z), a_6 = (Y, Z).$

Sketch digraph M.

13

13

Assignment

Name _____   Date _____

Isometric Drawings
Compositions

1. Draw the top, side, and front views of the isometric figure shown.

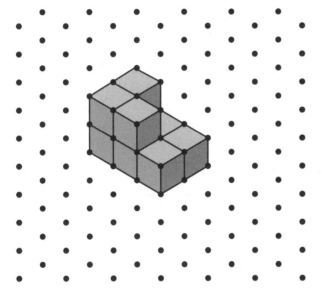

13

2. Draw the top, side, and front views of the isometric figure shown.

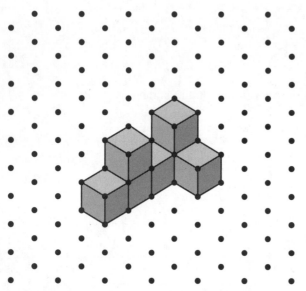

3. The top, side, and front views of a three-dimensional figure are shown.

Front View   Side View   Top View

a. How many cubes tall is this figure? Explain your resoning.

b. How many cubes wide is this figure? Explain your resoning.

13

c. Draw the three-dimensional figure on the isometric grid.

13

Assignment

Name _____ Date _____

Two Dimensions Meets Three Dimensions
Diagonals in Three Dimensions

1. What is the length of a three-dimensional diagonal of the rectangular prism shown?

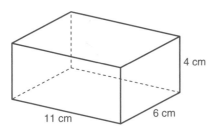

4 cm

11 cm   6 cm

2. What is the length of a three-dimensional diagonal of the rectangular prism shown?

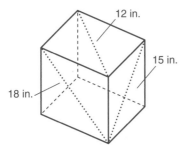

12 in.

15 in.

18 in.

13

3. A rectangular box has a length of 6 feet and a width of 2 feet. The length of a three-dimensional diagonal of the box is 7 feet. What is the height of the box?

4. The length of the diagonal across the front of a rectangular box is 20 inches, and the length of the diagonal across the side of the box is 15 inches. The length of a three-dimensional diagonal of the box is 23 inches. What is the length of the diagonal across the top of the box?

5. Pablo is packing for a business trip. He is almost finished packing when he realizes that he forgot to pack his umbrella. Before Pablo takes the time to repack his suitcase, he wants to know if the umbrella will fit in the suitcase. His suitcase is in the shape of a rectangular prism and has a length of 2 feet, a width of 1.5 feet, and a height of 0.75 foot. The umbrella is 30 inches long. Will the umbrella fit in Pablo's suitcase? Explain your reasoning.

13

Name _____ Date _____

By Air and By Sea
Introduction to Vectors

1. The initial point of vector w is $(0, 0)$ and the terminal point of vector w is $(-8, 5)$.

   a. Draw $\vec{w}$ on the grid. Label the initial and terminal points of $\vec{w}$.

   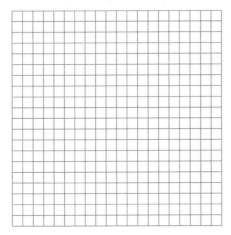

   b. Use vector notation to express $\vec{w}$ in component form.

   c. Express $\vec{w}$ in column vector notation.

   d. Determine the magnitude of $\vec{w}$.

14

e. Express $-\vec{w}$ in component form. Then draw $-\vec{w}$ on the grid in part (a). Label the initial and terminal points of $-\vec{w}$.

f. Draw a vector on the grid in part (a) that is equivalent to $\vec{w}$, but whose components are not the same as $\vec{w}$. Name this vector $\vec{v}$ and label its initial and terminal points.

2. Joshua is canoeing on a river due south at a rate of 6 feet per second.

a. Joshua encounters a current that is moving 1.2 feet per second due north. Describe the speed and direction that Joshua is moving with this current. Draw a diagram to represent the situation.

b. Joshua moves past the current and continues to canoe due south at his original speed of 6 feet per second. Then he encounters another current that is moving 2.8 feet per second due south. Describe the speed and direction that Joshua is moving with this current. Draw a diagram to represent the situation.

14

c. A large boat passes Joshua. The waves from the boat are moving 3 feet per second due east. Draw a diagram to represent Joshua's speed, the speed of the waves, and the vector resulting from Joshua's encounter with the waves.

14

14

Assignment

Name _____ Date _____

Adding Vectors
Adding and Subtracting Vectors

1. Consider vectors A and B, where $\vec{A} = \langle -8, 3 \rangle$ and $\vec{B} = \langle -2, -6 \rangle$.

   a. Calculate $\vec{A} + \vec{B}$.

   b. Use the Triangle Rule of Vector Addition on the grid shown to verify your answer in part (a).

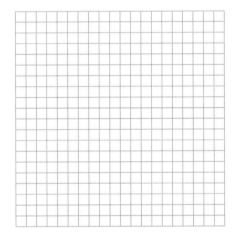

   c. Use the Parallelogram Rule of Vector Addition on the grid shown to verify your answer in part (a).

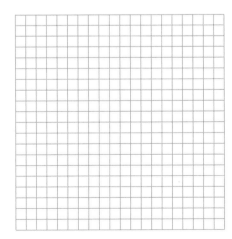

14

d. Calculate $\vec{A} - \vec{B}$.

e. Use the Triangle Rule of Vector Addition on the grid shown to verify your answer in part (d).

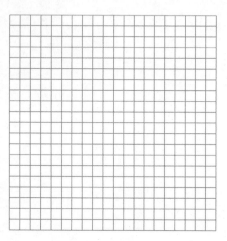

f. Use the Parallelogram Rule of Vector Addition on the grid shown to verify your answer in part (d).

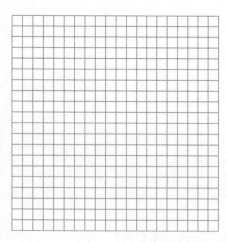

14

2. A cruise ship is traveling due west at a speed of 20 knots. (A knot is a measure of speed equal to approximately 1.151 miles per hour. Knots are commonly used to measure speeds at sea.) The cruise ship encounters a current traveling 3 knots due north. Calculate the resultant velocity and the direction of the cruise ship. Draw a diagram to represent this situation.

3. A helicopter is traveling at a speed of 85 miles per hour due east. The helicopter encounters a crosswind of 15 miles per hour due south.

   a. Calculate the resultant velocity and the direction of the helicopter. Draw a diagram to represent this situation.

   b. Calculate the angle between the helicopter's path due east and the helicopter's path with the crosswind.

14

14

© 2010 Carnegie Learning, Inc.

Assignment

Name _____ Date _____

SOS or Is It CQD?
Multiplying Vectors by Scalars

Use the given information to perform the indicated operation.

1. If $\vec{A} = \langle 10, -4 \rangle$, calculate $6\vec{A}$.

2. If $\vec{R} = \begin{pmatrix} -2 \\ 9 \end{pmatrix}$, calculate $-2\vec{R}$.

3. If $\left\| \vec{V} \right\| = 5$, calculate $\left\| 7\vec{V} \right\|$.

4. If $\vec{J} = \langle -1, 6 \rangle$ and $\vec{K} = \langle -2, -8 \rangle$, calculate $-3(\vec{J} + \vec{K})$.

5. If $\vec{P} = \begin{pmatrix} 4 \\ 0 \end{pmatrix}$ and $\vec{Q} = \begin{pmatrix} 2 \\ -3 \end{pmatrix}$, calculate $4(\vec{P} + \vec{Q})$.

Determine the components of the unit vector, $\vec{u}$, of the given vector, $\vec{v}$.

6. $\vec{V} = \langle 4, -3 \rangle$ 7. $\vec{V} = \langle 1, 7 \rangle$

14

8. $\vec{V} = \begin{pmatrix} -6 \\ -6 \end{pmatrix}$

9. $\vec{V} = \begin{pmatrix} -12 \\ 5 \end{pmatrix}$

10. The magnitude of vector w shown is 25. What are the components of vector w?

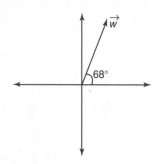

11. A patrol boat left the dock at point X and sailed to point Z. The patrol officer spotted a life raft at point Y. The officer immediately radioed his headquarters so that they could send a rescue boat. If $\overrightarrow{XZ} = \langle -20, -8 \rangle$, determine the components of the unit vector, $\overrightarrow{XY}$, to help headquarters locate the life raft.

© 2010 Carnegie Learning, Inc.

14